HE CLAIMED HER MOUTH AS IF IT WERE HIS RIGHT, HIS DESTINY. . . .

Del's pulse raced, her heart keeping tempo. For her, the moment revolved around a hazy, insatiable longing—a blind craving. . . .

His lips were persistent . . . unbelievably gentle, as his strong, sure arms encircled her, drawing her nearer, banishing the space between them. The warm, wondrous pressure of their consuming kiss intensified, becoming fevered, stripped of all restraint—a mutual admission of need. . . .

A CANDLELIGHT ECSTASY ROMANCE ®

LOVING ADVERSARIES

Eileen Bryan

A CANDLELIGHT ECSTASY ROMANCE ®

Published by
Dell Publishing Co., Inc.
1 Dag Hammarskjold Plaza
New York, New York 10017

ISBN: 0-440-14885-5

Printed in the United States of America

First printing—July 1983

Dedicated to the steadfast believer
whose technical advice and unwavering support
made this book a reality,
my husband

To Our Readers:

We have been delighted with your enthusiastic response to Candlelight Ecstasy Romances®, and we thank you for the interest you have shown in this exciting series.

In the upcoming months we will continue to present the distinctive sensuous love stories you have come to expect only from Ecstasy. We look forward to bringing you many more books from your favorite authors and also the very finest work from new authors of contemporary romantic fiction.

As always, we are striving to present the unique, absorbing love stories that you enjoy most—books that are more than ordinary romance.

Your suggestions and comments are always welcome. Please write to us at the address below.

Sincerely,

The Editors
Candlelight Romances
1 Dag Hammarskjold Plaza
New York, New York 10017

CHAPTER ONE

As Del Harris exited from the unmarked Ford sedan, the Gulf's night air cooled the flush stealing over her skin. Adjusting her shoulder-strap bag, she headed toward the station without a backward glance.

"Hey, Del, aren't ya forgettin' lover boy?" Deeder's singsong chant pursued her brisk steps, the implication in his voice stiffening her back. Determinedly she ignored the chiding grin separating his puffy cheeks.

"The pleasure's all yours, Deeder," she hollered back over her shoulder, carefully masking her mounting irritation. The last thing she needed to do was betray herself and give him any more ammunition.

"Come on, Romeo, let's git this over with." Assuming responsibility, Deeder hauled the pale-faced prisoner from the car as Del pushed the combination to the door lock and entered the station.

It was that peculiar time of night, shortly after a change of watch, when an eerie amnesty settled over the station. In thirty minutes the halls would be bustling with the action of the graveyard shift, but at the moment only the solitary rat-a-tat-tat of a typewriter from the records section and Del's tattooed step upon the terrazzo floor broke the stillness. Outside the detective squad room Del hesitated. Then, with a composing breath and an exaggerated push upon the door, she breezed into the office. Horton barely looked up from his newspaper and coffee. Steneski, sitting with resoled shoes atop the desk, reclined farther back in his chair and never broke stroke as he continued flipping paper clips, one by one, into the wastepaper can.

Tossing her purse on the desk, she briefly scanned her awaiting messages and then proceeded to stroll toward the bathroom. Once inside, she locked the door (a habit she'd learned the hard way after a few embarrassing incidents) and quickly turned on the basin spigots. Only then did she venture a look into the mirror. Damn! Her cheeks were still stained a vibrant red! Good old Deeder had done it again.

Furiously she pressed the soap dispenser, releasing an avalanche of dry white flakes into her hand and beginning to scrub with the care of a surgeon. An absurd picture of Lady Macbeth, lathering over and over to erase the effects of her dirty work, flashed into her head. Above the gush of lukewarm water she could hear the conversation in the outer office. Deeder was beginning to describe what had happened with great dramatization and a fair amount of elaboration. Oh, yes, she knew exactly how the story was going. She'd heard Deeder's tall tales many times before.

"We'd stopped off at Leisure's café for a bite to eat, Del fussin' the whole while about cohabitatin' with wharf riff-raff and spoutin' public health standards. But bein' my usual persuasive self, I win out in the end. Well, she can't wait to split. So I tell her to go on outside and cool off while I take care of the check.

"Now here comes the good part. While she's hangin' around outside, this young punk figures her for a lady of the evenin'. Swear to God! He hits on her, and by the time I mosey on out she's readin' the kid his Miranda rights.

I tell ya I'da given a month's pay to have seen the look on Casanova's face when she flashed her shield!"

A burst of laughter momentarily interrupted Deeder's folksy narration. "I ain't finished. It gits better. Turns out the kid's the son of Thurman Vance . . . District Court Judge Thurman Vance. . . . He tells her straight out his daddy ain't gonna take kindly to her harassin' him. Then Junior turns to me and says, 'How're ya supposed to know the *man* when he's wearin' a skirt?. I take one look at Del and decide it's best to ease clear. 'Son,' I says, 'late at night on the streets it's pret' near impossible to distinguish.' "

Another round of grating laughter invaded the bathroom. Roughly patting her hands on a paper towel, Del Harris blindly focused into the mirror. Her usually passive nutmeg eyes glinted dangerously. *Five years,* she thought. *Five years, and I'm still fighting for acceptance.*

She'd worked her way up: a street cop, then juvenile officer, and finally passing the sergeant's examination. But that hadn't exempted Del from the prejudice, voiced and unvoiced, to which a female officer was subjected. Though now, more times than not, the men laughed with her instead of at her, the fact remained that they still laughed.

She'd been good-natured, taking the sexist remarks in stride and the practical jokes with good humor. She knew they thought her a good cop, but she still represented an invasion of their domain. At a knock upon the door Del snapped from her introspection.

"Hey, Del, I know it's a unisex bathroom, but if you're just primpin', hurry up! I gotta git in there." A long sigh passed her lips as she pressed her cool hands to her cheeks, then crossed and unlocked the door. With a calm smile she brushed past Deeder's mischievous wink.

As she returned to her desk, it was obvious that Horton and Steneski were strangely preoccupied with paper work. A foreboding crept over her. It was the calm before the storm. She knew they couldn't resist an opportunity to ride her.

She settled behind her desk, concentrated on writing the report, and tried to ignore the low exchange coming from across the room.

"You smell something funny, Horton?" Steneski sniffed the air like a bloodhound.

Del kept her head bent, the bold strokes upon the report intensifying.

"Yeah, now that you mention it, I do. It's kinda familiar, but I can't quite place it." Horton's baby blues twinkled above the dark hollows emphasizing his eyes.

"You smell it, Del?" Steneski turned to her with an innocent cock of his head.

She pretended not to hear, shifting her trim figure within the chair and continuing to add details to the report.

"Maybe she's wearing some new fragrance?" Horton suggested, setting Steneski up.

"Mmmm, mmmm! Kinda sensuous, ain't it?" Steneski drew a deep breath.

Horton mimicked, exclaiming, "Provocative! Why, I do believe she's sportin' Vance Junior's favorite—Eau d'Entrapment." The two broke into uproarious laughter.

With the utmost restraint Del set aside her pen, glancing up from the report with a smile that didn't quite reach her eyes.

"Only the two of you could appreciate it," came her tart retaliation, inciting another surge of chuckles until the phone on Horton's desk intervened.

"Detectives, Sergeant Horton." There was a long pause, followed by a curt "Yeah, I got it," before he slammed down the receiver. "Come on, Ski, we got a homicide over at the Arlington Arms. Sure hope it ain't another whodunit," he muttered sarcastically, grabbing his sportcoat from the back of the chair.

"Have fun, boys," Del purred, resting her heart-shaped chin on a hand and savoring their retreat as Deeder reentered the room.

"Where they headed?"

"You mean now or eventually?" she quipped, returning her attention to the report in an ill attempt to hide a satisfied grin.

"I know where they're gonna end up. I meant now. Want some of this warmed-over mud they call coffee?"

"Only if you tame it with some of that powdered cream. Junior tucked in tight?"

"Just like a baby. He's insistin' on his one phone call, probably to his influential daddy. Del, you ain't real sore about my funnin' ya, are ya?" He handed her a mug of liquid which sufficed as coffee, then slouched to a chair in front of her desk.

"Course not, Deed," she lied. "You add the only excitement in my life."

"Yeah, well, that's your fault. A good-lookin' dame like you ought to be home rubbin' her old man's back." He paused, grinning wide, and added, "Or rubbin' somethin'."

"You ever think about anything else, Deeder?"

"Sure, eatin' and sleepin'—speakin' of which, I'm way overdue for both. Ya see, unlike you, I'm totally undedicated, unprincipled, and looking forward to my old lady's back rubs. Twenty-two years, and I still can't get enough."

"Back rubs?"

"Hell, no, but close!" He laughed, rising from his chair and hoisting his pants above his rounded paunch. "Ya off for the next couple of days, huh?"

"'Fraid so. You'll just have to struggle through without me," she said teasingly.

"Junior's gonna miss ya, but I'll be sure to give him

your regards." He shot her a devilish look before shuffling toward the door.

A disgusted grunt and a penetrating glare were all he received in answer.

"Sometimes you're hard down unsociable, Del." His parting gibe preceded the slam of the door.

For a long, thoughtful moment she sat staring at the door, her reproachful expression replaced by an affectionate smile.

Deeder and she had been partners for more than a year now, and in spite of his unorthodox ways, she'd grown very fond of him. A short-timer, with retirement only months around the corner, Deeder had developed a complex street philosophy that combined the moral preaching of an Arbor Lights missionary, the cynicism of a red-neck, and the folksy wit of a laid-back southerner.

He'd witnessed every cruel, bizarre, or comical incident, handled the spectrum of details. Yet throughout it all he'd managed to remain human enough to cope and survive, unlike some of the other men, who'd eventually regressed to barely a cut above the elements they protected society from.

Though he took a little getting used to, and a heck of a lot of patience, his loyalty and infinite knowledge warranted the effort. There wasn't another officer on the force who had the contacts or instinctive sixth sense that Deeder possessed. She'd learned quite a bit from him. Even so, she knew that she hadn't begun to tap the wealthy reserve of beat-cop experience harbored within the man.

During their association she'd watched the pro work his magic—gaining a snitch's confidence by relating on his level, soothing irate complainants with calm, humorous logic, and asserting authority whenever the situation forced his hand. Yes, Deeder definitely personified a cop for all seasons, and it saddened Del to think he'd reached the autumn of his career. A tired sigh escaped her as she returned her attention to the endless paper work.

The reports, though routine and automatic, filled up as much time as the actual investigations. Del doubted a cop existed who didn't hate the boring task, but it came with the territory. Tonight, for some odd reason, she found it difficult to concentrate amid the quiet solitude of the deserted office.

A good-lookin' dame like you ought to be home rubbin' her old man's back. Deeder's blunt observation swam through her head.

He'd always mocked her ironclad rule of never becoming involved with other cops. Even when she'd argue that an arrangement of that sort only complicated a professional relationship, he'd counter with "Aww, come off it, Del. Who better understands the pressures?" Then he'd take it a step farther. "Okay, fine! Then pick ya out a regular Joe, some eight-to-five exec type—ambitious and climbin'." And when all else failed, he'd resort to piercing her womanly pride. "Wise up, Del! It don't have to be the love of your life—but it just ain't natural for a woman to be sleeping alone."

Del flipped through the paper work and methodically began to place report sheets in the proper folders. As always, she pushed the negativeness of her personal life into the deeper recesses of her mind. This was the method she used to avoid thinking about her romantic impotency. This way her traumatic secret remained locked within and guarded against discovery.

Aimlessly she ran a hand through the rebellious honey blond curls she'd always hated. Now labeled the "natural look," her wispy hairdo passed as vogue, and therefore, she tolerated the curly halo for the time being. Her eyes drifted to the panorama beyond the windows: the slow-paced metropolis of Corpus Christi glittering against the velvet black of a lazy southern night. When she was off duty, not much awaited her out there, except a modest town house on the west side, an old mama cat, and thirty more monthly notes on an '80 Cutlass.

Tiredly she rubbed the back of her neck. A frown flitted over her features at the ache between her shoulder blades. She glanced behind at the air-conditioning vent that targeted intermittent blasts at her. From her first day in detectives, she'd been bombarded by the frigid current. She had always suspected that the guys had given her the best desk in the house with sadistic intentions in mind.

She rose from the chair, determined to rectify the situation once and for all. Only one small obstacle stood in her way: the height of the vent. She scanned the room in search of a stationary chair, but only pedestal types on casters offered themselves. Deciding the accomplishment far outweighed the risk, she wheeled a chair directly beneath the vent. Then, with the dexterity of a high-wire performer, she slipped off her shoes, hiked her skirt, and climbed atop, balancing precariously as she inched a hand up toward the vent. Obstinately the lever held itself a hair's breadth from her fingertips. She stretched farther . . . then a little more. She'd have it in a second, but within that second the chair rotated, sending her toppling backward with arms flailing and a low curse hanging suspended.

Suddenly and surely a strong arm caught her about the waist. The brace was effortlessly easy as her unseen savior cradled her slender figure against a rock-hard support and then gently lowered her feet to solid ground. A wordless exchange passed during that fleeting moment—a sensory conduction that blazed in a touch and left an indelible brand on the soul. The steel band about her midsection lingered, withdrawing only as she turned to face a mesmerizing, glacial gaze, the color of which was undefinable

—not blue or gray, but an indescribable blend of both. It took her by storm, the ensuing breathlessness causing her timid "thank you" to sound embarrassingly inadequate.

"You're quite welcome." The words emanated from a mouth that curved in an engaging smile. Del struggled to detach her gaze, seizing upon fumbling for her shoes as an excuse.

"I'm glad I happened along when I did. Actually I'm hunting a Sergeant Harris. I was told I could find him here."

Now it was Del's turn to smile as she slipped a foot into a Wedgie. Her rescuer's attention rested on the ample portion of leg revealed through the front slit of her skirt, but a curt "You've found her" quickly altered his focal point. Surprise flickered across his striking features for an instant, quickly replaced by an expression of poise and even amusement.

"It seems I have not only good timing but good fortune as well." His smooth reply regained the advantage.

With a lift of her chin Del shook off the compliment, taking her seat and gesturing for him to do the same. "What can I do for you?" she asked, reverting to a professional, "just-the-facts" routine.

"I was told at the booking desk that you've got a hold on Judge Vance's son. I'd like to make arrangements for his release." He set a linen-textured calling card on her desk.

Curiously she picked it up and ran a polished fingertip over the raised lettering: "Mitchell Parrish, Attorney at Law." Immediately black on white headlines flashed in her head: CELBETTI ACQUITTED ON TECHNICALITY; STRATEGIC DEFENSE TACTIC WINS MISTRIAL FOR DR. LUNSFORD; PARRISH PREDICTS NOT GUILTY VERDICT IN CARGIN OIL HEIRESS CASE—all sensational trials defended by Parrish and all won on technicalities, brutal discrediting of witnesses, and brilliant summations.

"Mitchell Parrish," she repeated slowly, with recognition.

"You say my name with familiarity, though we've never met. I'd certainly remember if we had." He smiled warmly, yet his eyes remained impassive.

"Your reputation precedes you, Counselor." She flipped the card back across the desk and pretended to rearrange already sorted paper work. "A solicitation charge is somewhat out of your realm, isn't it, Mr. Parrish? Are you fulfilling some charitable commitment or just slumming?" Del wondered what made it impossible for her to look up from the camouflage of business and meet his disturbing gaze.

"I'm here on an errand of friendship. While you might call it charity, I prefer to call it a favor." Though eloquent, his voice held distinct reproachfulness.

At that inopportune moment a folder slipped from her shaking hands, scattering various pieces of paper work over the floor. Embarrassed, she inwardly cursed her schoolgirl jitters while bending to retrieve the mess. To her further humiliation, in his attempt to help, Mitchell Parrish and she met at the side of her desk—crouching low, grasping the same sheet of paper at opposite ends, and foolishly staring into each other's eyes. Again the blue-gray depths drank her in, diffused, and dissolved her. Momentarily she became lost in the strange, immobolizing effect this man seemed to have over her.

"You tend to be a little accident-prone," he said chidingly, his tanned cheek only inches from hers, enabling her to distinguish the pleasing scent of his cologne.

"It's late, and I'm numb from overtime. Thank you again." She withdrew, making another unnecessary commotion while restacking the folders. The tension between them escalated with each passing silent second.

"I'm here to do my job, Sergeant Harris." Parrish's drawl became persuasively mellow. "My only intention is to get my client and myself home tonight. I'm sure you'd like that, too. So, for the good of all concerned, can we dispose of the matter?" He reseated himself on the edge of her desk, too close for comfort and near enough to exert pressure.

Hastily she scribbled "bondable" across the appropriate copy. "It's taken care of, Counselor. Will there be anything else?"

"Not unless you'd care to join me for a late supper?" The request denoted neither eagerness nor complacency.

"Thank you, but I've already eaten," she replied aloofly.

"Too bad. Perhaps another time. Good night, Sergeant." He stood, commandingly tall, superbly toned, and incredibly handsome.

This was a man whose confident bearing transmitted irrefutable maleness, his handsome features emitting not only intelligence but charisma. Yes, here was an individual who bore his dynamism as casually as he sported his expensive attire—each perfectly tailored to fit the singularness of the man.

He seemed a contradiction—obvious yet obscure. But was he obviously obscure or obscurely obvious? Del's mind reeled with inexplicable questions. Why, against her will, were her thoughts and senses completely filled with this man's presence? His blatant masculinity making her all too keenly aware of her own femininity? The unspoken stimulus his very nearness exuded both domineering and exciting her? A crazy one-word description tripped into her head—"*taboo*" . . . set apart, prohibited. It was the essence of the man, the captivating awe which made him so dangerously appealing.

For an instant Del Harris seriously considered retracting her refusal of his dinner offer. A slow smile drew across his sensuous lips—almost as if he could read her mind. Instinctively Del bristled, shifting papers in a dismissing gesture.

"Good night, Counselor!" She feigned absorption in her duties. An amused glimmer shaded his eyes a brilliant blue. But because she never lifted hers until she heard the click of the door, she missed the counselor's warning trait. In the future she would learn it was a telltale clue of intrigued interest. For Mitchell Parrish thrived on challenge, in court and out.

It was exactly a week to the day when Del next encountered the infamous counselor. Armed with a subpoena in her jacket pocket, the report of young Vance's misdemeanor in her attaché case, and a strange premonition in the back of her mind, she climbed the endless steps leading to the contemporary courthouse.

There was a weariness about her stride that went beyond physical exertion—a defeatism that transcended boredom. This was her third trip this week to testify on behalf of the state, and somehow she couldn't shake the doomed feeling that this last trek would, most likely, round out a trilogy of futility.

As Del swung through the plate-glass doors, the muted sounds of justice in the works surrounded her. As she meandered by huddled groups of jurors and witnesses, victims and DAs, defendants and counselors, snatches of conversations drifted into her consciousness.

"What d'ya mean we could lose?" an outraged victim lamented. "I get mugged, and you're preaching constitutional rights?"

"Hey, man, I tol' ya. I robbed her, sure, but I never laid a hand on her! I ain't taking no assault rap!" An accused pleaded qualified innocence.

"Shoot me your best deal . . ." said a seasoned defense attorney.

"Okay, have him plead guilty, and I'll reduce the theft charge to a class A misdemeanor," a harassed prosecutor offered.

Del always found it fascinating—the extent of legal dickering that took place in the hall. Sometimes more justice was administered in these public corridors than inside the judge's domain.

"Sergeant Harris, wait up!" The breathless entreaty came from behind, halfway down the hall. Del drew up and turned to face the plump figure of Preston Simms, the assistant DA whose misfortune it was to be assigned to the Vance case.

"No wonder y'all wear out so much shoe leather. I've been chasing you all over this place. And I tell you, I'm in no condition." The wan smile that touched his lips matched the dowdiness of his dress. Though assistant DA's salaries were meager, Simms's attire was ridiculous. He always looked like a bargain-basement reject.

"I'm sorry. I didn't hear you call. I had some things on my mind." She scooted closer to allow a harried defendant and her counsel to pass.

"I was holding those quaas for a friend. They weren't mine. How can they convict me of possession?" Del had heard it all before—not from the same lips, but before.

"You were saying, Prosecutor . . ." She regained the plump DA's attention as he, too, had become lost in the melodrama.

"Ah, yes." He ran a hand through his prematurely thinning hair. "We need to parley, Sergeant. Not here, though." His meaningful gaze swept their bustling surroundings. "I've confiscated an anteroom at the end of the hall. Follow me, please." He spun on his run-down heels and led the way.

Her earlier premonition grew stronger as she followed—a trilogy of futility. No sooner had she stepped inside the small cubicle than her uneasiness became validated. Rising from his station at a plain table, Mitchell Parrish greeted her with a diplomatic smile and his customary ease.

"Nice to see you again, Sergeant. I hope this impromptu meeting hasn't inconvenienced you?"

Unconsciously Del tightened her grip on her attaché case. "Not at all, Mr. Parrish," she replied politely.

"Well, since all parties are present and accounted for, let's begin, shall we?" The pudgy DA took a seat upon a slatted straight-backed chair and began to shuffle papers absentmindedly. With a nervous look up at the still-standing adversaries, he attempted a puny stab at humor. "I think we'd negotiate better on the same level. Why don't we *all* sit down?"

Gallantly Mitchell pulled out a chair. With equaled decorum Del accepted, easing herself onto the hard slats and crossing one shapely leg over the other. Though she kept her eyes trained on the rumpled DA, she was cautious enough to retain Mitchell Parrish in her peripheral view.

Locating the file he'd misplaced, Simms ceremoniously cleared his throat before addressing Del. "Sergeant, what are your feelings about an adjudicated sentence for Vance?"

From the corner of her eye Del noticed Mitchell's disconcerting study of her legs. She shifted in her chair, repeating the DA's words like a mockingbird. "An adjudicated sentence . . ."

"Yes, well, all that simply means is that if the defendant successfully serves out the terms of his probated sentence, there'll be no record."

At that moment Mitchell also shifted position, his posture seemingly relaxed but vigilant. The personal vibrations he transmitted were much more poignant than the professional negotiations taking place. Del's attention hovered somewhere between the two.

"I understand what the term means, Mr. Simms," she answered dryly while pointedly refusing to meet the counselor's magnetic gaze.

"Uh-huh," the DA mumbled, flipping through the papers before him. "Well, then, if you have no objection, I'm prepared to offer Counsel the reduced sentence in return for a guilty plea. After all, the accused is young, has no prior offenses, was obviously intoxicated at the time, and . . . well, I'm sure Judge Vance would appreciate a speedy and uncomplicated end to the whole matter."

Not until the last reference did Del react. At the mention of the judge she sat straighter in her chair. Mitch did not miss the move or the opportunity to rectify the DA's tactlessness.

"The judge's feelings in this matter are inconsequential," he said smoothly. "What is important is that my client realizes his brashness, and if the sergeant is agreeable, I think he will be properly reformed by the embarrassment of this ordeal."

For the first time Del faced the legendary counselor. Strangely he appeared not as notorious as he had been depicted, but rather amiable and genuinely concerned. His logic was well founded; his appeal, minimal and direct. She really had no wish to be hard on young Vance. By reputation, she knew his father's disapproving anger was probably punishment enough.

"I have no objections, gentlemen. The terms are fair. I'll leave young Vance's fate in your hands." She met Mitch's gaze head-on and felt her pulse quicken at the admiring gleam she collided with. Quickly she looked away. "If that's all . . ." Del left the sentence hanging as she groped for the attaché case she'd set by the side of the chair.

"Yes, well, I think that about covers it," the DA was muttering while closing the file. "I thank you for your cooperation, Sergeant."

With an easy retrieval of the truant briefcase Mitch stood and extended it toward her. "I'll do better than a thank-you, Sergeant. I'll buy you lunch."

With an anxious clutch of the leather case Del attempted once again to decline. "Really, it's not necessary. I've already—"

"I know," he interrupted, shooting her a perceiving smile as he leaned to shake Simms's stubby hand. "She's probably already eaten." He grinned into the puzzled features of the DA.

In a commanding gesture he caught her elbow and escorted her toward the door. "Then at least come keep me company." At the doorway his hand casually cupped her arm. It wasn't a forward move, merely gracious. Dazedly Del found herself accompanying him, his masterly presence beside her not at all unpleasant. There was a mystique about this man—an unfamiliar energy that kept her perpetually unsettled.

Throughout the brief yet hazy jaunt to the restaurant Mitch carried the brunt of the conversation, Del only occasionally adding a monotoned and superfluous comment. Not until they were seated at a small table for two in a cozy eatery profusely filled with greenery did Del realize how easily she'd been manipulated. With his usual dominance Mitch had ordered for them both. He'd also charmed the waitress into bringing a wedge of cheddar to accompany their carafe of Chablis.

Mentally shaking herself, Del emerged from the lethargy she'd escaped into. "You really shouldn't have ordered for me. I was serious about having already eaten."

He leaned closer over the table to study her for a conspicuous moment. She prayed her prideful fib didn't show. "Is it that I have an unfortunate sense of timing? Or have you an insatiable appetite? It seems no matter the hour, you've just eaten." He cocked his head suspiciously.

"What can I say?" She feigned a lightness she didn't feel. "Working girls have hearty appetites."

"Your slimness certainly doesn't substantiate the claim," he said challengingly.

"Nervous energy," she quipped, thankful that the waitress's timely appearance necessitated his leaning back in his chair and postponing his rebuttal. As requested, two long-stemmed glasses of Chablis were set before them, and a generous wedge of cheese arranged on a wooden board in the center of the linen tablecloth.

Mitch flashed the waitress an approving smile as Del's jaw tightened. She declined his offer of a slice of cheese with a curt shake of her head, choosing instead to take a fortifying sip of her wine.

"Tell me, Sergeant, why is it that every time we encounter each other I sense this overwhelming hostility emanating from you? Is it defense attorneys in general or me in particular that rubs you wrong?"

Del almost choked on her wine. Easing the glass to the table, she refrained from looking up from its sparkling contents when answering. "I wouldn't exactly call it hostility, Mr. Parrish."

"Mitch," he requested.

"Mitch," she said in compliance. "To be perfectly honest, I'm afraid my assessment of you as an attorney is somewhat biased—based on headlines and station house gossip. As for you, the individual? I hardly know you." She chanced a glance across the table. He looked amused.

"Fair enough, I suppose." He half laughed. "And easily rectified. Let's begin by laying to rest a few misconceptions about myself. I plead guilty to being an ambitious lawyer who built a reputation by taking on unpopular or bizarre cases. Perhaps I was a little overzealous early in my career. It's been said that I had a flare for the dramatic. Actually I think I was merely compensating for an insecurity." He nibbled the cheese while baiting her interest.

"I can't imagine you insecure," she prompted.

"Even now I still have my moments." His eyes made contact, seconding the innuendo. Del's gaze trailed to her wineglass.

"I'm not offering excuses, only an explanation. My flare for the dramatic attracted the press. Sensational headlines sell newspapers. My acquittals gave them those headlines; the press gave me publicity. In the process I became something more than merely an attorney with a good track record; I became a personality. It's been my ticket and my albatross."

"Are you always so philosophical?" She sipped from her glass once more.

"Not always. I just thought if I presented the facts, it might temper your judgment of me."

Opportunely the food arrived and spared her from the intensity of his blue eyes. As lunch was served, Del fought to compose her jangled nerves. This man impressed her—his pleasant drawl, his easy carriage, his polished manners. And yet . . . there was a blatant challenge about him—like a neon road sign that flashed "Dangerous Intersection Ahead." If she was smart, she'd detour, but her heart accelerated as his knee brushed hers beneath the table.

"It's your turn to tell me a little about yourself." He slowly savored the wine as she toyed with the food upon her plate.

"I wouldn't make nearly as interesting conversation as

you, Counselor. I'm uniformly ordinary," she said, hedging.

"I doubt that. What made you choose to become a police officer?" His pursuit was relentless.

"It's a family tradition. My mother died when I was very young. I was an only child, reared by an Irish beat cop; it just seemed the natural order of things."

"Your father must be very proud."

"He might have been."

An uncomfortable pause stymied them both. Suddenly the tête-à-tête had become very serious. "I'm sure he would have been." The sincerity of Mitch's comment equaled the understanding reflected on his face. Tactfully he switched topics. "Simms hinted that you might soon be the first female lieutenant in the department. Is this fact or merely speculation?"

"Well, I'm eligible to take the upcoming exam. You might say I'm determined to give the *chauvinists* some competition." A sudden pensiveness altered his expression. Observing the abrupt change, Del grew apprehensive. "Surely you're not one of those men who feel that ambitious woman are unfeminine?" she asked probingly.

"Not if they keep it in the proper perspective," he admitted candidly. Then, quickly, he added frankly, "I've known a few individuals whose ambition made them oblivious to everything and everyone else. I don't find that a particularly admirable quality in men or women."

"Are you intimating that I may be one of those types?" Her Irish temper began to rise.

"No," he drawled. "You asked my opinion, and I'm merely responding. I never judge a person that quickly."

His reluctance to commit himself had an intensely opposite effect on her. "There are degrees of ambition," she said reflectively. "I don't consider myself obsessed with my career, but I am determined. I'm not sure it's proper, but at the moment my profession is a very big part of my life."

As he assimilated her views, Mitch's blue-gray eyes grew opaque. Engrossed with the significant part of herself she'd unintentionally revealed, he failed to realize that he'd yet to reply.

Del hadn't the vaguest notion of why his sudden mood change upset her, but it did. It was as if his approval mattered; that, of course, was absolutely absurd. Inexplicably a casual lunch, shared with a near stranger, had taken on a definite personal implications, something she preferred to avoid. Considering her present frame of mind, she decided it would be best to excuse herself and end the conversation, for that matter, sever this brief association before it became unduly complicated.

"I thank you for the lunch, Mitch. I hate to eat and run"—she dabbed her lips with the napkin, then tossed it aside—"but I'm already overdue at the station." She muddled through a fabricated excuse. Why was she behaving so irrationally? And why did he continue to stare at her in such a curious manner?

"It was my pleasure." He came to his feet.

In her haste to escape Del once again fumbled for her misplaced attaché case. For a second time he came to her rescue, standing before her and offering the elusive article.

Holding her hand out, Del strived for nonchalance. "Thank you again." In lieu of the briefcase, his warm hand clasped hers. Whatever she had expected in response, it certainly was not what she received.

With a disarming smile he left her with a final thought. "I would imagine that you've had to work twice as hard, as well as overcome numerous obstacles and prejudices, to have a shot at this lieutenant's position. I wish you much luck."

Momentarily stunned by his unsolicited support, Del

stared numbly up at him. Only the withdrawal of his hand andthe placement of her briefcase in her grip prompted her timid "Yes, well, all things considered, a little luck certainly couldn't hurt. Good-bye, Counselor."

"I'll try not to take that permanently." He grinned.

In spite of herself, she had to smile. Lord, but he was an impressive man.

CHAPTER TWO

The setting sun cast a soft amber glow as serene as the lazy stretch old Mama Cat gave when rising from her siesta. A Kenny Rogers tape played on the stereo, and an issue of *Cosmopolitan* lay deserted beside a forsaken teacup on the coffee table. All the ingredients of normality were visible, all except Del's usual complacency.

Slim fingers tucked into the back pockets of her jeans, she sauntered about the den discontentedly. Normally she hoarded her precious off-duty hours like a miser. It was to her the equivalent of R and R after five days at the front. This evening, however, the town house retreat had become more like a prison, the four walls closing in and her nerves as edgy as an inmate's.

Moodily her gaze roamed her surroundings. The furnishings were chic; the decor was subtly earth-toned, and each minute accent a reflection of her individuality. Altogether the room revealed the domestic side of the hard-shelled professional. For it reflected tireless hours devoted to artistic and feminine labors of love—fragile butterflies under glass; cozy, crocheted afghans; and engravings of self-composed verse. Yet this evening even the loving touches couldn't alleviate the emptiness that needled Del from within.

With a heavy sigh she flopped among the gay pillows scattered across the couch and disinterestedly began to browse through the magazine she'd abandoned earlier. She hadn't bothered to change from her morning attire of faded jeans and a scooped-neck T-shirt with the words "Anything boys can do, girls can do better!" stenciled across its front. Her hairstyle was equally as casual, arranged in a floppy pile atop her head and secured with tortoiseshell combs, with corn silk wisps feathering about her face.

Idly her fingertips played with the escaping tendrils at the nape of her neck as her eyes randomly scanned one article after another. The title "How Does Your Social Life Measure Up?" jumped out at her with a turn of the page. She sighed resignedly at the thought of yet another quiz which rated one's performance on a scale from one to ten. Somehow she always ended up ranking somewhere between less than average and a total loser. For some sadistic reason Del found herself reaching for a pen on the coffee table, but just moments later the unfamiliar sound of her doorbell caught her, pen poised over question one. Even Mama Cat took a break from her supper, perking her ears at the strange chime and watching interestedly as Del took curious steps toward the door.

With a turn of the knob an astonished Del faced her unexpected caller: the striking Mitchell Parrish, perched on her doorstep and toting a large brown grocery sack.

"Evening, Sergeant." He greeted her in a casual voice. "Since we missed one dinner date, I took the liberty of arranging another." A mischievous smile curled about his lips as he gazed upon her attractive but plainly shocked features. "Please don't tell me that you've already eaten again," he rushed on. "I can't possibly consume all this myself, and worse yet, I'd be forced to dine alone."

"How did you find out where I live?" The stunned

words fell from Del's slightly agape mouth, while impolitely she detained him on the doorstep.

"It wasn't difficult," Mitch said, hedging. "You had better ask me in. I think the butter's melting." He slipped through the partially open door, proceeding straight toward the kitchen as if he'd known where he was going.

Utterly speechless, Del shut the door and followed, staring in disbelief as he began to unload his welcome-wagon sack.

"Red wine!" He passed a French-labeled bottle before her eyes. "Perfect accompaniment for my version of a stakeout—two T-bones, thick and lean." A butcher-paper-wrapped package hit the counter.

Still unable to collect herself after his overwhelming entrance, Del numbly repeated her original question. "I asked how you found me."

"I never compromise confidentiality," Mitch replied blandly and then evasively changed the subject. "You do have a barbecue pit, don't you?" he asked matter-of-factly, seemingly oblivious to her bewildered state.

A nod of honey blond curls preceded her next monosyllabic question. "Why?"

"Simple." He grinned, walking to the pantry, again as if he'd known its exact location, and retrieving the aluminum foil from the shelf. "Barbecuing seals in the flavor and doesn't make a horrendous mess in the kitchen. We can even bake the potatoes in the hot coals." His large hands efficiently went about blanketing the brown-skinned vegetables in the shiny wrap.

"No! I mean, why did you bother to look me up?" The gradual regaining of Del's composure was evidenced by the cocky lift of her chin and keen cut of her brown eyes.

"Excuse me for a minute. I have to get the charcoal from the car." Tactically he withdrew, retracing his steps toward the front door. "Finish unpacking the salad fixings, will you?" came the distant command. Still suffering from momentary disorientation, she complied like an obedient child.

In a few minutes she heard him puttering about on the patio. As if of their own volition, her eyes were drawn to his form beyond the glass door. Dressed in form-fitting jeans and an open-necked grippered western shirt, he went about his chore with confidence. Automatically Del's hands ran the lettuce under the water, but her gaze remained riveted on his lithe figure outside: the powerful legs covered in denim; broad shoulders, and trim waist; the sinewy flow of muscles beneath a plaid shirt; and the ebon sheen of perfectly styled hair edging the nape of a manly neck—in totality, the dynamic projection of masculinity in motion.

Suddenly saturated lettuce leaves draped her hands. Frustrated by her unusually intense fascination with a man's anatomy, she hit the spigot with a bang, flopped the wilted lettuce into a colander, and exasperatedly wiped her hands on a cup towel.

Mitch reentered, his blue-gray eyes assessing Del as he washed his hands at the sink. Mama Cat braved a closer look. Tentatively she weaved through the giant stranger's legs, but as Mitch leaned down to pet her, the calico merely stuck her tail haughtily into the air and pranced off.

"I don't think he can make up his mind whether he likes me or not." Mitch laughed, drying his hands and beginning to unwrap the steaks.

"He is a she, and that makes two of us who are undecided about you, Mr. Parrish." Del's arms crossed over her chest in an obstinate gesture.

"I like cautious females. They're seldom given to hysterics. And don't you think Mitch would be easier, Del?" He never looked up, securing the salt and pepper shakers from the lazy Susan on the counter and beginning to season the meat. "I like your T-shirt, too, a little ostentatious, but definitely challenging." He dared a peek from out of the corner of his eye and caught her immediate reaction—a slightly huffier stance.

"Did you discover my first name by your amateur investigative methods, or are you psychic?" Her voice became defensive.

"Neither," he replied, reaching to the spice rack and pondering over a selection. "I asked at the booking desk."

"You've gone to a lot of trouble to find out about me, Counselor. Once again, may I ask why?"

He began to sprinkle a concoction of spices over the meat. "I have no devious or ulterior motives, I can assure you. I find you attractive, intelligent, and a bit of a mystery. Therefore, I'm enchanted and more than a little intrigued."

Del eyed him suspiciously as she countered coolly, "I'm not quite sure—was that another one of your brilliant orations or merely the laying of groundwork?"

"Both." He grinned, his eyes shading predominantly blue. "I think I should check the fire. Why don't you do the honors and pour the wine? I'll be right back." Again he deserted her on the edge of uncertainty.

As Del went through the motions of uncorking the wine bottle, her frustration mounted with each unsuccessful attempt. She applied more pressure to the corkscrew, grimacing and muttering her displeasure. Mama Cat cocked her head curiously, licked her paw, and began to wash her ears.

"I don't need this aggravation!" She fumed, afraid Mitch would return at any moment to find her struggling. "Anything boys can do, girls can do better!" she repeated breathlessly, tugging with all her might until a blessed pop! filled the air.

With a sigh of relief she stretched for the top shelf of the cabinet, but only empty space met the fingertips that searched for the stored glasses. An undignified obscenity accompanied her tomboyish mount of the counter top.

It was this unladylike pose that struck Mitchell Parrish as he silently returned to the room. Amused by her predicament, he relaxed against the opposite counter and smiled to himself while enjoying the view. A rascally twinkle highlighted his eyes with each curvaceous maneuver of her derrière, but wisely he extinguished the incriminating gleam at her final scoot and slowly lowering leg.

"I'll bet you were some tree climber in your youth," he said teasingly, his unexpected presence startling Del and almost causing her to lose her balance at the last second. He reached out a supportive hand, once again creating the electric current that volted through both their bodies.

"And I'll bet you were an angelic-faced devil who never got caught at pranks!" Del snapped, unnerved by his intense effect.

Mitch's spontaneous laugh filled the awkward gap. Assertively he took the glasses from her unsteady hands and poured the wine. With a disarming smile he passed her a long-stemmed goblet and raised his. "To the best in life and those who have the patience to wait their turn."

Del found his words odd, but the wine excellent. For a significant moment their gazes locked over the edge of the goblets. Mitchell Parrish was beyond a doubt the most attractive man ever to have entered Del's life. Yet he also represented everything she despised within the legal system: a man totally devoid of moral conviction, who, regardless of the degree of guilt or innocence involved, sold his services to the highest bidder. Without question, he symbolized her fiercest ideological adversary. As she looked upon his handsome features, she found it preposterous that they were sharing the wine and this moment.

Nothing quite so extraordinary had happened to her in a long, long time. Quickly she lowered her gaze, then the glass, wondering what Mitchell's thoughts were.

"How are you at making salads?" His voice interrupted her contemplation as he set aside the vintage wine and picked up the mass of dilapidated leaves which once had been a firm head of lettuce. "What happened to this?"

Sipping her wine for reinforcement, she averted her contrite gaze. "I may have overdone it a little."

His laugh rang light and genuine. "If you'll get me a bowl, we'll see what we can salvage." In seconds his request was filled, and Del and he conversed amiably while shredding, peeling, and slicing in unison.

"You have a nice place here, Del."

"I like it."

"I suppose cops don't have much leisure time, do they?"

"Not much. Our irregular hours make a social life difficult."

"Do you enjoy your job, Del?" He noted her hesitation before replying.

"For the most part, yes," came the soft admission.

"And when you don't, why is that?" he pursued.

Del sprinkled bean sprouts over the top of the salad. "Sometimes it's hard to remain a believer when everything around you is being made a mockery of."

"Is that how you think of yourself—a believer?" Mitch's congenial expression became somber.

"In a sense, but lately I'm beginning to wonder if 'dreamer' wouldn't be a better description." She stared into the shimmering contents within her glass, her words seemingly more directed to herself than to him.

"You sound disillusioned." Curiosity and concern mingled in his gaze.

She tossed her head, bouncing the loose fluff of curls on top and raising her eyes to meet his.

"I was just thinking aloud. One of those cursed privileges of being a loner, I guess." God! She wished she could retract that last revealing statement.

An odd smile curved his full mouth, almost as if he had sensed her silent recrimination. "I know," was all he said, picking up the salad bowl and depositing it in the refrigerator. "You've been that most of your life, haven't you?" At her incredulous look he clarified. "A loner," he explained. "Skirting the edge of congeniality, but never venturing across that thin line that separates acquaintances from friends."

Though his words pierced, Del controlled a wince. "It seems your talents are endless—a psychologist as well as a supersleuth. Amazing!" she said cuttingly.

"Elementary, my dear Watson." He grinned, casually perching himself atop the counter, then patting its surface in an invitation for her to join him.

"This is ridiculous," she scoffed, boosting herself to the counter top. "I do have chairs."

"But this is cozier," he said cajolingly. "There is something about a kitchen that puts people at ease. I remember my family gathered around our kitchen table to celebrate, or commiserate, whatever the occasion dictated. Back then I wasn't the loner I am now. The difference between you and me being that my ivory tower was by choice." His perception of her was uncanny.

"Why do you keep dwelling on the topic? Do I come across as antisocial or eccentric?"

"I'd say 'reserved' and, most definitely, 'private' would be a better description."

"And private people bother you?" she asked with a hint of sarcasm.

"They interest me," he corrected. "Mainly because they create unanswered questions."

"Such as?"

"Such as, why an attractive and bright woman like yourself makes no mention of any other man in her life except her father; no goal but a professional one."

"Oh, but I believe we've already covered those questions." Her reply was direct; her eyes were evasive.

He cocked his head curiously, at which she interjected, "Ambition, pure and simple, Mitch."

An easy smile pulled at the corners of his mouth. "Though the answer may be pure and simple, I have a feeling that an explanation would be complex."

"Are you leading the witness?" She saluted his efforts with a mocking hoist of her wineglass.

"Establishing motive." He returned the courtesy.

"Which is?" Del demanded.

He contemplated her for a disturbing moment, as if unsure whether to proceed. Then, swallowing the last of his wine, Mitch offered a theory. "I think that ever since you were a little girl, you've had to be more mature, more capable than your years—a young lady of the house who was the apple of her daddy's eye. I'd be willing to bet that you compensated for being deprived of a mother's gentle influence by gaining attention through achievement and thereby winning your father's praise. Accomplishment, and its subsequent reward, gave you a sense of security which carried over into your adult life."

He noted Del's patronizing smile, yet doubted its authenticity. "As for the men in your life . . . something tells me that they've been few, casual, and far between. I'm guessing that there might have been one who was more special, but then the relationship turned sour, leaving you disillusioned and less willing than ever to trust in love again."

He'd struck a nerve. The brief play of emotion that flickered across her face confirmed it.

"My, but you can build a hypothetical case, Counselor," she said flippantly. "I can certainly see why you've been labeled as dramatic." In an easy move she swung to the floor. "Now I have a question: Am I being defended or maligned?"

"Neither." He smiled. "I'm merely conjecturing."

"May I also?" A mischievous glint sparked her brown eyes.

"Certainly," Mitch assented, his expression amused as he relinquished control.

"Why would an attorney who has already proved himself continue to seek out cases which test and exploit the system? And why would such a man, who's been publicized as being popular with the ladies, while away a potentially exciting evening to theorize about and dine with a recluse?"

Gaining confidence and momentum, Del began to pace anticipatingly. Her unintentional mime of a prosecutor summarizing a case necessitated the lowering of Mitch's dark head to conceal his mirth. "You've lured my curiosity. Please enlighten me," he prodded.

"It's my contention that in his youth such a man was indulged and coddled beyond belief . . . that advantages came too easily and without satisfaction. Therefore, he became attracted to the controversial and thrived on triumphing over conventionality."

Slowly Mitch raised his gaze to hers, a sobering reflection in his eyes. Del paused indecisively, but at his encouraging nod she continued.

"As for the women in his life . . . I would assume there've been many—mostly shallow types with great bodies and one-track minds . . . certainly pleasurable company, but hardly stimulating."

Mitch quirked a brow. She ignored his reaction. "So it is feasible to suspect that when, by sheer chance, the restless attorney meets the atypical cop, it is no more than an interesting diversion." Del took a deep breath and, with a challenging look, rested her case.

In an agile move Mitch eased his large frame to the floor. After a few tense seconds without comment they simultaneously began to smile.

"I think our debate has left more questions than answers," Mitch offered, the inflection in his voice half-teasing, half-serious.

"Yes, it would seem so," she agreed. "Do you find yourself wondering what we've accomplished?" A note of true bewilderment toned the question.

With a gentle press of her arm Mitch replied, "In legal terms we've managed to create a reasonable doubt. But more importantly, Del," he said in a softened tone, "we've established a premise, and once we prove or disprove the theories, the verdict will become clear. But I think for now the jury's still out." His touch lingered as his eyes captured hers. For the first time Del realized the full impact of Mitch's persuasive power.

"It's about time for me to put on the steaks. Don't go away." For the third time his tall figure retreated on cue.

Del refilled their glasses and took them along as she wandered into the darkened living room. She snapped on a soft-glowing lamp, then proceeded to the stereo and slipped a new cartridge into the tape deck. The low, melodious notes of her favorite song filled the room. Del stood listening, sipping her wine and beginning to sway to the music.

"It was smooth, mellow music . . . The hurt rememberin' kind . . . Easy, slow swayin' words of another place and time . . ."

The sentimental words swirled like the red, red wine in the glass within her hands. Eyes closed, Del momentarily drifted until the foreign feel of Mitch's arm slipping around her slim waist broke the trance and brought her eyes abruptly open.

"Could I have this dance?" he asked in a low voice, exerting no physical pressure, yet psychologically asserting his will.

Her first impulse was to shy away, but her mind argued: *Why not? It's been a long time between dances.* She smiled, set her glass atop the stereo, and assumed the position.

They moved in rhythm, their bodies a perfect blend of complementing contours and steps. Again she became acutely aware of his scent, his touch, his warm breathing fanning her hair.

"As we pressed our bodies close, in my arms I held her tight . . . And we moved like we were one, somehow it felt so right . . . For though we were strangers with pasts that were done . . . We knew we shared much more than just the dance we'd begun . . ." The taunting words mingled with the distant sound of Mitch's voice.

"It's been a long time since I've danced for any reason other than courtesy's sake. I'd forgotten how good it can feel."

She raised her eyes to his, a silent understanding reflected within. Before either realized, the words stilled, the music ended, yet the special mood remained.

"Play it again," Mitch urged. "I think it's becoming my favorite."

She slipped from his arms and skipped the tape to the soft, slow strands once more. Then, in almost a hypnotic approach, she returned to his embrace and the waltzing moves which somehow were so easy to follow.

"Dear old friend, mellow music, play it easy and slow . . . As I hold on to this woman . . . For God only knows . . . How I needed this moment, how I needed a friend . . . Now it's all within my arms . . . Come on, please play again."

He pressed closer. She could feel the tautness of his muscular chest, each breath he took. Quietly he hummed to the stirring words, his cheek nestling against her hair, his shallow breaths wisping her ear. She melted nearer, unaware that he, too, could feel the thudding vibrations of her excited heart. Their moves became slower, more natural—the soft light, sentimental music, two glasses of wine side by side, swirling, blending, and creating the aura of romance that swept them beyond the hostile strangers that they were.

"Play on, play again . . . For old times' sake, my friend . . . Create for us new memories . . . While mellow music plays again . . ."

A contented stillness settled over two opposite rooms and the individuals within as Mitch sat relaxing upon the couch after dinner and Del went about returning the decorative bowl of fruit to the kitchen table.

Mitch studied the creative treasures displayed about the comfortable den, deducing more about the person with whom he'd just shared the intimate dinner than he'd learned from the pleasantries of table talk. Anyone who had created such beauty with her own two hands harbored a gentle sensitivity and loving nature deep inside. Funny, but he did not find that fact surprising. He'd sensed a multifaceted personality in Del from the first moment they'd met. Maybe she was exactly as she'd described, but in reverse: a dreamer, trying to remain a believer. Whatever, she was, as he had stated, a bit of a mystery.

Del inspected the tidied kitchen once more before leaning to blow out the dwindling flame of the candle. Her eyes fell on the profile of her unexpected dinner companion, now relaxed upon the couch and idly stroking the calico. In a glance she took in the high, intelligent forehead, classic straight nose, angled cheekbones, and rigid, set chin—overall, the cameo of an educated, well-bred, and forceful man. But the defined profile only hinted at the magnetism of him. Without being able to look into the blue-gray depths that were the nucleus of Mitchell Parrish, one missed the paradox that made him both godlike and mortal at the same time. Noting his restless stretch, Del blew out the candle and went to join him on the couch.

"And how does your social life measure up?" he asked, a hint of goading in his voice as he eyed the opened pages of the magazine resting between them.

Taken by surprise and half-embarrassed, she prudently closed the periodical and flipped it atop others on the coffee table.

"I don't know. I haven't taken the test." Purposely she omitted the fact that only reason she hadn't was his unexpected arrival.

He glanced at the assortment of magazines before fixing her with a penetrating look. "Well, if the only choices under consideration are a measure-up exam in *Cosmo* or who's who in *Texas Lawman,* I'd say your social life leaves much to be desired."

A blush crept over Del's cheeks, but the defensive retort ready on the tip of her tongue went unsaid because of his tactful switching of topics.

"How old are you, Del?" Mitch turned to face her, one leg propped on the edge of the couch and his arm draped casually over the back. His half-opened shirt revealed a virile mat of dark hair upon his upper chest. With each breath he took, the laced chain suspended from about his neck gleamed contrastingly golden in the lamplight's reflection.

"I'll be thirty-five the end of this month," she replied, shifting her gaze and trying to appear as relaxed as he when settling against the pillows.

"That would make you a Libra. If I remember my signs—artistic, domestic, and a hopeless romantic." His smile grew warm and attentive.

Del stiffened, her nutmeg eyes flashing as she scoffed, "And you're a—"

"An Aquarius," he interjected. "A realist in the truest sense of the word, who'll be thirty-three in February and loves older women!"

Mama Cat roused, stretched, and leaped for quieter ground. The interruption gave Del a moment to gather her wits, Mitch's humor winning out in the end and tempering her initial urge to snap back testily.

"You're very opinionated about women, Counselor. Correct me if I'm wrong, but so far you've stated a preference for maturity, cautiousness, and challenge. What other qualities must a woman possess in order to meet your high standards?" A devilish fire lit her dark eyes as she raised them defiantly to his.

A slow, condescending smile spread across his full lips as he eased nearer. Suggestively his fingertips caressed an errant golden tress at the nape of her neck. Del realized her mistake too late. Helplessly she found herself ensnared by his hypnotic eyes.

"A gypsy soul," he answered in a mellow voice.

"Very poetic, Counselor. What does it mean?" Quizzically Del stared up into the charismatic angles of his face. The shadowed effect cast by the muted lamplight made him appear excitingly ominous.

"I'm referring to the old saying 'Eyes are the window to the soul.' Yours speak of a fiery spirit, a nomadic existence." His gaze fell to her lips, his words becoming pensive and lulling.

"Melancholy eyes that lure like a violin's haunting serenade." His face grew nearer, his seductive mouth hovering inches from hers.

"An expression within them: an intimation of smoldering passion—untamed and exciting. Gypsy eyes," he whispered, tenderly brushing her awaiting lips and igniting a long-ago abandoned emotion. "Dark reflections of a gypsy soul."

He claimed her mouth as if it were his right, his destiny. His lips were persistent . . . unbelievably gentle, as his strong, sure arms encircled her, drawing her nearer and banishing the divide between them. The warm, wondrous pressure of their consuming kiss intensified, becoming fevered, stripped of all restraint—a mutual admission of need.

Languidly his supple tongue traced the smooth concaves of her mouth, its salacious pressure reawakening an essential vital part of her innermost being which had long been neglected. The heady effect begged to be recognized, and of its own volition, her mouth parted farther as her tongue reciprocated in kind.

Mitch's adept fingers cradled her nape, guiding her kiss and reinforcing its searching depth. When they released her, it was only for an instant to slip beneath the back of her T-shirt and allow his fingertips to communicate his desire with each inching stroke.

His touch left tingling trails along her responsive flesh and a sweet ache in her heart. Traitorously Del's body writhed at each and every point of his caress. With a soft moan she surrendered to the coaxing massage, melting closer . . . closer still . . . until cleaving to his muscled form. Their breaths came in unison, the momentum increasing as they became lost in the specialness of "first discovery." It was a fleeting instant of ecstasy, soon to become lost in time and yet forever cherished in their hearts.

Del's pulse raced, her heart keeping tempo. For her, the moment evolved around a hazy, insatiable longing—a blind craving for an experience which had been deprived her by years of irrational fear. But only for a few delirious seconds did she topple into the chasm of spontaneous passion before fear, mistrust, and reality reclaimed her.

Like a burn victim, she cringed from the source of heat, the back of her hand shielding her lips from his branding kiss.

"What is it, Del?" Confusion marked Mitch's voice as his smoky eyes searched her distraught features.

Quickly she removed herself from his embrace. She walked to the picture window, focusing blankly into the darkness beyond while fighting for composure. In an attempt to hide the spasmodic panic knotting in the pit of her stomach, she wrapped her arms about her midsection for support and then forced her reply to sound flippant.

"Oh, it's been called many things—being a tease . . . frigid . . . a cool number. Take your pick!" God! She despised the sound of her own voice. What had she become in order to survive an ordeal which mentally gripped her like a steel vise?

She heard his move from the couch, her heart pounding erratically as she sensed his approach. Consciously she stifled a sigh of relief at his guarded halt a few steps behind.

"Del . . ." Her name came as softly as his light touch upon her stiff shoulders. Slowly he turned her toward him. "I sensed nothing abnormal or vindictive in the woman I just kissed. I make my living by observing and reading people. What I recognized in you a moment ago was plain, unadulterated fear. I recall the same trapped expression in the soft eyes of a doe I'd zeroed in my sights one season—an instant of vulnerability and doomed premonition."

Del's chin quivered. The truth cut too deeply. Never lifting her eyes, she murmured, "It's late, Mitch."

Gently he tipped her chin, his gaze a blend of distress and optimism as he replied, "Yes, as far as tonight goes,

I agree, but I don't concede anything more. There is a dormant gypsy inside you, Del. She's only awaiting the right moment to emerge and the special man who'll discover and understand her. For future reference remember his name—Mitchell Parrish."

After having made his prediction of what the future held, he released her chin and climactically walked for the door.

"You're very sure of yourself, Counselor," she said accusingly, staring dazedly at his departing back.

"Yes, ma'am, I am," he drawled, shooting her a meaningful wink before softly shutting the door.

CHAPTER THREE

"'Twere them aliens, ma'am!" The ludicrous statement jolted Del from the lethargy of mundane procedure. The penciled notations she'd been jotting in the notebook came to an abrupt halt. She looked up into the deadpan features of the health food shop's elderly proprietor, then cut to Deeder, who turned his head in a timely coughing seizure.

"Aliens," she repeated matter-of-factly, careful to avert her eyes to the notebook.

"Yes'm! Not the first time them devils broke in here neither. They're after my elixir. I didn't report it the first time, but seein' as how they're acomin' back, I figure it's my duty—national security 'n' all. That stuff's mighty potent, ma'am. Not a bit atellin' what energizin' effects it could have on them heathens."

In the course of following up on routine investigations, Del had run into her fair share of loonies before, but this was shaping up to set the record. She could feel Deeder's amused gaze on her and knew he was enjoying watching her sweat her way through.

Calmly she continued. "Any signs of forced entry, Mr. Matlock?"

"No, ma'am. I figure they vaporize 'n' come in through

the air ducts. They kin do most anything they've a mind to, ya know."

Smiling patronizingly at the old fellow, Deeder reached into his pocket for a can of Skoal and began to pinch a dip. "So we've been told, Mr. Matlock," he muttered, placing the shredded tobacco inside his lower lip and relaxing against the counter as he smugly awaited Del's next move.

An impish solution occurred to Del. Closing her notebook, she gave Deeder a quick glance of warning, then presented her most professional self to the dotty proprietor.

"You're very fortunate, Mr. Matlock, in that my partner made this call. Sergeant Deeder Hanes heads up an IAP special task force within our department. That stands for Investigations of Alien Phenomena. He'll be following through on this incident, and if in the future you have any further problems of this nature, feel free to report all pertinent information to him directly. It saves unnecessary red tape and helps us work more closely with conscientious citizens like yourself. We'll be in touch, Mr. Matlock, and try to have a good day."

"Yes'm, and thank you. Be callin' you soon as I got somethin' more to report, Sergeant Hanes."

"Yeah, ah, you do that," Deeder managed to say, following Del's springing steps out of the shop to the unmarked sedan. A splat of tobacco juice hit the pavement before he yanked open the door and settled behind the wheel.

Del picked up the mike, announcing in a clear voice, "One-oh-five back in service."

A static "One-oh-five . . . clear," answered as Deeder started the motor and eased out into the afternoon traffic.

"Okay, we're even, Del. Pretty smooth work back there, but did you have to tag me with him?"

"Can't see as I had a choice, Deeder." Her smile broadened as she purposefully kept her eyes focused on the stream of traffic ahead.

"Oh, you had a choice all right, hot dog!" He grinned, keeping an ear cocked to the dispatcher's intermittent communiqué.

"You're always calling me that, Deed. I don't know whether to be insulted or complimented. What's it mean?"

Deeder hung a left, swinging toward the heart of town. "A hot dog's a crusader—pumped up, full of vim and vigor. Yeah, he's out to change the world and make it the decent place we've all dreamed of in principle and become disillusioned with as time goes by. All recruits are hot dogs—gung ho to cop by the book and see justice served."

He slowed for the yellow caution light, glancing at Del with a professorial expression.

"Problem is, most learn after a year or two that justice has two heads and dragon slayers are generally pretty unpopular. To be effective, ya gotta learn a street code—a combination of bendin', blendin', and renderin' justice on a day-to-day, call-to-call basis. Survival of the fittest and earned respect from those within as well as outside of the law, that's what coppin's all about."

The light turned green, and Deeder laid his foot on the pedal.

"Ya been around long enough to have had your armor pierced some, hot dog. You're a real slow learner!" His fatherly lecture ended, he shot her a concerned look before growing silent once more.

"Maybe so, Deed," she admitted, crumbling under his knowing eyes and glancing away.

The sedan cruised down the central business district, the static radio garble keeping them company along the way.

"Listen, Del, it's almost time to knock off. What do ya say to swingin' by the courthouse? There's a big case being tried this afternoon that I'd kinda like to sit in on. Narcotics made a bust on a Colombian connection, and to an old ex-narc like myself that's just pure stimulatin'. Course, Sanchez is only a mule. . . ." He paused, the teacher in him taking the time to clarify. "A mule's a delivery boy, but the pressure's on 'cause somebody's frontin' him a lethal mouthpiece by the name of Parrish. Ya ever heard of him?"

Del straightened the hem of her skirt, mumbling, "Mmmm, I've heard of him."

Oblivious to her fidgeting, Deeder rambled on. "This thing's been draggin' on forever, but I think the showdown's gonna be today. Ya mind stoppin' off for a few minutes?" He glanced at her with childlike expectancy.

"Sure, why not?" she replied, trying to ignore the acceleration of her heartbeat as the car sped in the direction of the county courthouse.

Within a few minutes Deeder and she approached Courtroom D, where the trial had been in progress for a short time. Excited though he was, Deeder had the gentlemanly presence to hold open the enormous oak door and allow Del first entry. The room was filled to capacity, and not a head turned as they moved to join the standing-room-only spectators hugging the perimeter of the huge hall.

Just as they found a place from which to view the proceedings, the tall figure of Mitchell Parrish, clad in a vested gray pinstriped suit, arose from his chair at the defense table at the front of the room. His commanding voice rang out distinctly and clearly, its effect almost echo-like by the time it traveled the distance to the rear of the room where she and Deeder were standing.

"Your honor," he began, his posture easy, his manner totally confident, "at this time I would like to request a motion for dismissal of the charge against my client, Dolphus Emanuel Sanchez."

A low murmur circulated through the room. The young assistant DA leaned forward attentively as Judge Wright peered over his Benjamin Franklin frames, glancing from the prosecutor's table to Parrish.

"On what premise do you base your motion, Mr. Parrish?" The predictable response came from the bench.

Mitchell Parrish approached the high podium and passed an official document to the bailiff, who in turn handed it to Judge Wright.

Beside Del, Deeder shifted restlessly, muttering beneath his breath, "Auh, oh!" Del's observant brown eyes darted to the dark-complected defendant slouching cockily in his chair. She wondered if she only imagined the smug expression on his hardened features as he ran a hand through his unkempt black mane.

"I bring to Your Honor's attention a recent ruling by the Texas Court of Criminal Appeals which concludes that the word 'cocaine' has no definitive meaning within the law. Since the obtained search warrant issued to the investigative officers and subsequent indictment handed down by the grand jury contained, and pertinently phrased, the aforementioned word, I believe the charge to be invalid and, as such, my client should be awarded an immediate dismissal."

The shocked DA jumped to his feet, "I object, Your Honor!" he shouted. Parrish turned to face him, his eyes as steely as his gray suit and a deceptive, neutral expression frozen across his carved features.

"The use of the word 'cocaine' is irrelevant. The defendant is charged with the possession and sale of a controlled substance. Counselor's fine-line terminology has no bearing on the alleged felony at issue here."

A sense of anticipation settled over the hushed chambers, the tension mounting as all eyes focused on the two opposing forces limelighted within the legal arena.

Judge Wright set aside the document, removed his glasses, then closed his eyes and thoughtfully massaged the bridge of his nose for a few seconds. In a heavy, almost burdened voice he rendered his decision.

"I'm afraid I must overrule your objection, Mr. Prosecutor. Though I, too, am of the conviction that the terminology used in the indictment has been prevalently adopted and allowed, it is now interpreted as not having a meaning within the law. Therefore, I have no choice but to declare the indictment invalid and to grant Counselor's motion for a dismissal." With a hollow strike of the gavel the decision became final.

The assistant DA sank to his chair, the absolute devastation of intolerable defeat mimed in his resigned pose. Aghast spectators turned to one another in disbelief. Deeder straightened his slumped shoulders, gave a low grunt, and exchanged glances with his ex-comrades as they looked to him for support. Del stood immobile, staring at the only unaffected figure in the entire courtroom as he slowly returned to his table, shook Sanchez's hand, and tidied up paper work.

"Come on, let's git the heck out of here!" Deeder gave a disgusted shrug before taking a step to join the slow stream of spectators filing toward the door.

Del touched his arm in a detaining gesture. "You go ahead, Deed. I just remembered some unfinished business I need to tend to." Noting his hesitation, she urged, "Go on, I'll hitch a ride. I think your buddies could use a stiff drink about now." She nodded toward the dejected group of narcs congregated by the door.

"Yeah, they do look kinda pathetic. If ya git stranded, give me a holler down at the Waterin' Hole."

"Sure thing," she promised, taking a second to watch

his peculiar shuffle before returning her attention across the emptying space between her and Mitchell Parrish.

Isolated and preoccupied, the infamous counselor was engaged in conversation with his client. Del glared openly at the two. Resentful ire mounted by the second, kindling her unwavering gaze to fiery pitch. At that precise moment Mitch snapped shut his briefcase in a concluding gesture and glanced in her direction. Immediate recognition registered upon his face in the form of a seldom seen public smile. With a lanky stride he breezed through the swinging gate and walked directly toward her. Del tried to ignore the odd sensation his very approach ignited—something akin to early warning tremors of a catastrophic quake.

"Hello." He greeted when within a few feet of her. "Fancy meeting you in a place like this."

"Why, if it isn't the perpetually unpredictable, always victorious counselor! Tell me, Mitchell Parrish, does this win make you even more invincible?" Del's condemnation came in short, seething breaths, her animated eyes betraying her contempt of his latest sensational defense.

Somehow, without her being aware, his hand grasped her elbow, firmly escorting her out the courtroom doors. Once beyond, his sure grip led her to a deserted corridor, Mitchell taking a position between her and the exit before finally relinquishing his hold.

"Your temper's showing, Sergeant. I don't think this is the time or place to display a childish tantrum. For some ridiculously immature reason you seem to be taking whatever happened in there personally. Do you mind telling me why?"

Del's chin rose. "You're unbelievable, do you know that?" she snarled, her venom permeating the hallowed atmosphere of the marbled halls. "What a pompous intellectual you are—waltzing in there in your expensive

Brooks Brothers suit, presenting your eloquent libertarian case, dazzling the ignorant public like a magician pulling a rabbit out of a silk hat!

"You'll excuse me if I don't applaud your performance, Counselor. But all I see is an ego trip that managed to undo hours of surveillance and months of sacrificing patience. In a few short minutes you've nullified a combined effort of overworked, underpaid, and often ostracized men whose only sustenance is a gut-level belief in what they do. Unlike you, they'll never know public recognition, and because of your total disregard for justice, they'll not even savor a moment of personal satisfaction. You ought to feel real proud of yourself when you think of how many naïve kids you've just handed over to that scum you've just freed!"

Her tirade ended, Del tried to sidestep the object of her scorn, but again an iron grasp impeded her forward movement.

"Hold it, Sergeant!" His frigid tone denied any escape. "I want to explain a few things to you. I'm retained to defend a *client* to the best of my ability, *not my methods!* Everyone"—he paused, his intent gaze engaging and holding hers—"everyone is entitled to a defense . . . is presumed innocent until proved guilty. Therefore, when a prospective client comes to me for aid, I proceed within that assumption.

"What of the enviable heiress handicapped by wealth and status, the press screaming for her blood? Would you deny her the same option as the deprived, persecuted minorities whom the public magnanimously makes allowances for? How about the targeted cop who's accused of being on the take—one lousy bribe? Is he automatically excluded from representation, precondemned, because John Q. Public will not tolerate an alleged tarnishing of an exalted example?

"Prejudices come in all forms, Miss Harris. The virus isn't isolated; rather, it's contagious and rampant. Guilty or innocent, influential or ordinary, don't they each deserve the best defense money can buy? And believe this, when I go into that courtroom, that's exactly what they get—a no-holds-barred all-out effort. Yes, I use every angle, tactic, or diversion at my disposal and within the extreme limits of the law because I'm out to win—win freedom for them!"

"And I suppose you're presumptuous enough to expect a commendation of those efforts?" she scoffed.

"I never presume, Sergeant," he said in clarification, then quickly added, "But I did expect you to recognize the fallacy within the law."

"Shifting blame? How unworthy of you, Counselor." Fanatical in her denunciation of him, Del neatly overlooked his valid point.

"I'm merely placing the emphasis where it belongs. We both know that this technical win is but the first round in a lengthy bout. Sanchez will be reindicted, correctly next time, and eventually retried. The entire procedure is a ridiculous waste of the taxpayers' money and the court's time. And all because of a minute legislative loophole. Are we in agreement so far?" He waited.

Del obstinately refused to commit herself. "Go on," was all she'd concede.

Undeterred, he continued. "These setbacks are unfortunate, but not irreparable. Luckily this particular technicality has been brought to light before a consequential case might be lost. Sanchez is small-time . . . immaterial really; it's the *precedent* of his defense that's important here. Because of the publicity my motion for dismissal will surely receive, that law will be amended."

His explanation made sense. A tinge of guilt made Del question her slanted incrimination of him. Still, he was a clever adversary. He could merely be giving lip service to a cause that conveniently suited his purpose.

"Are you telling me that you sacrificed yet another portion of your already dubious reputation in order to expose a potentially disastrous loophole in the law?" She searched his face for a sign of confirmation.

His expression retained its practiced passivity. This was one judgment he wouldn't attempt to sway. Even though it happened that he had true conviction on his side, his pride and patience had limits.

"All I'm saying is that the law needs to be amended, *and quickly.* It's not entirely the legislature's fault. What appears to be incontestable on paper is, sometimes, debatable when put to the test in a court of law." The pressure on her arm relented, a strange blueness intermingling with the hard gray within his eyes as he added, "And now that we've debated the scales of justice, I'll see you to your car. Believe it or not, I still observe a few amenities."

"That's not necessary," came the curt retort, backed up by a hostile glare.

"Now you really are behaving childishly." A goading grin broke his striking features.

"I am not!" she snapped defensively, making a mental effort to curb the urge to stamp her foot.

"What would you call it then?" His dark brow arched accusingly.

"Being practical. You see, Counselor, at the moment I'm without transportation. So there's no need for you to walk me anywhere."

"In that case I'll drive you home."

"Thank you, but again it's not necessary." Del began to walk away.

"Are you so hardheaded that you'd prefer to walk?" Mitch caught up to her in two long strides.

She continued her brisk pace, stubbornly ignoring him. "I've a friend I can call," she parried coolly.

"You've a friend who's offering." His hand touched her arm in much the same fashion that his simple statement touched her heart—light and warm, persistent and sensitive.

Their eyes made contact, the silent question within hers answered by the subtle blue tinting his. "Is it possible for us to be friends?" a searching gaze asked. "Not only possible, but as probable as the morning sunrise," a steady gleam of indigo confirmed a moment before a guiding hand initiated the forward steps which could never be retraced.

Del sat staring at the dancing flames within the rustic stone hearth until a loud pop of cedar, followed by a burst of orange sparks, broke her concentration. In wide-eyed awe her gaze roamed the unique den of Mitch's bayfront hacienda. She missed nothing—from the highly polished floor of russet brick to the center fountain tiled in Aztec blue and circled by a lush indoor garden.

The blazing firelight alternately highlighted, then shadowed the distinctive rectangular enclosure. Along three paneled walls hung an extensive collection of Mexican folk art. A glassed fourth wall provided a glimpse of the moonlit bay beneath half-raised woven woods striped white, blue, and russet. Del became more and more intrigued as she took in the sleek contemporary furnishings, the priceless Indian artifacts. Strains of Bach filtered from the stereo. The stark contrasts were an expression in themselves.

Another crackle of sparking cedar drew her attention to the oak mantel. Atop the veneered ledge rested leatherbound editions of Tolstoy's *War and Peace*, Steinbeck's *Grapes of Wrath*, and Harper Lee's *To Kill a Mockingbird*.

At opposite ends stood gilded picture frames, one preserving a souvenir program from a performance of *Madama Butterfly;* the other, a photograph of an impressive sloop christened *Latin Lady.*

There seemed to be many facets to the hacienda's owner, and that diversity stimulated Del's imagination. She resituated herself upon the enormous pillow in front of the fire and stretched her stockinged feet toward the warmth. Contentedly she closed her eyes and savored the serenity, but only briefly, as telltale footsteps heralded Mitch's return.

"Crazy, isn't it, how northers blow in unexpectedly and drop the temperature so quickly? Down here on the bay it seems even cooler than the actual readings. Thought you might enjoy a mug of hot buttered rum with me." He set a tray containing appetizers and the steaming brew on the stone edge of the fireplace and then sank to the pillow beside her.

He'd changed into a cashmere sweater of light gray, the banded sleeves pushed midway up his lower arm. Del imagined him to be the kind of man who couldn't stand constraints of any kind—even about his wrists. His charcoal corduroys were wide-wale and matched his suede loafers perfectly. In the soft glow of the firelight he appeared casual and relaxed and exceptionally handsome. Quickly Del's gaze became glued to the dancing flames once more.

"You always seem to be feeding me like some orphan waif." She broke the silence while reaching for her mug. "This smells delicious. I've never drunk hot rum before, but I doubt there'll be a more perfect moment." She smiled, sipped, then rested the mug on her knee.

"I suspect that there are many things you've yet to experience, many I'd enjoy introducing you to." Noting her skeptical look, he smoothly went on. "What makes the moment perfect is the presence of a beautiful woman to share it with." He raised his mug in salute before tasting its potent contents.

Del couldn't decide if he mocked or complimented her, but it became unimportant when, for the first time, she noticed the ring on his little finger. Made of sterling silver and set in turquoise stones, it was wide, almost to the knuckle, and odd in design.

"Your ring is very unusual. Indian, isn't it?" She noted the brief taut expression about his eyes a second before he replied.

"Yes, Indian. It was gift given to me a long time ago." His words drifted.

"By a special lady, I'll bet." Del didn't know what made her say the last, but once having done so, she studied his reaction. Nothing! Only a presented profile as he now presumed to contemplate the blazing ballet as intently as she had.

"Yes, once she was very special, but only to me. Now . . . she's adored by millions." Though softly spoken, the words betrayed a harbored bitterness. He started, as if suddenly realizing his reminiscing had been voiced and embarrassed by the revelation. "The rum's much better if you drink it while it's warm."

Graciously she humored his whim, finding the buttery flavor pleasing, the heated liquor soothing. But, her curiosity peaked, Del couldn't resist broaching the taboo subject once more.

"Then, at least, one theory has been disproved." Mitch's perplexed look told her he'd forgotten their kitchen debate. "My assumption that all your female companions were inconsequential," she reminded him.

"Yes, well . . ." Atypically he stumbled over his words. "It seems we've laid one misconception to rest," he finally admitted. He pondered the bottom of his mug a moment before elaborating further. "Why not clear the slate?" He spoke as if to himself. "Yes, there have been a substantial number of women in my life. And yes, except for one, none of them meant anything. You were correct in your assumption that I was restless and searching when we met, but that is as far as your accuracy goes."

His steely gaze bore through her. Suddenly she wished she hadn't pressed him for this intimate admission. "I categorically deny that I found you merely an interesting diversion." He paused, claiming her gaze and anticipation. "I found you fascinating," he confessed. "In light of my honesty, don't I deserve a few truths?"

Del's heart skipped a beat as a sporadic thought skitted through her mind: *truth or consequences.* The unexpectedness of his entreaty mandated an honest reply. She drew a deep breath. "Your theory that there have been few men in my life . . . that much is true. I confess that I'm a loner, not so much by choice as by habit. And yes, in some ways I'm insecure." The last admission came with obvious difficulty.

"Everyone is at some time or phase in their life, Del. I'm curious. When is it that you feel most secure, more at peace with yourself?" he asked, probing a little deeper. Observing her withdrawal from the question, he said cajolingly, "Mine is when I'm sailing. The schooner is sturdy and swift, the wind cool and salty, that vast stretch of open water a highway in any direction I choose to go. There is a freedom about it that restores and invigorates me. It's a time when I'm accountable to no one."

His spontaneous sharing prompted her to do the same. "My moments are far less robust. I guess I feel it most at the end of an especially hard but fruitful day . . . a kind of day when you feel that you actually made a difference. Maybe it was in only one person's life, but you changed that life for the better somehow. To have that kind of effect, if only now and then, makes me feel necessary and special."

Mitch turned to her. As he half rested on an elbow with a knee propped, his fingers idly played with lace border of the slip that coquettishly peeked from beneath her pleated skirt.

"You're special to me, Del. A moment ago, when I referred to your beauty, I wasn't just making fireside chat. I find I am very susceptible to that intriguing aura that seems to surround you. Ever since I was a small boy, I never could resist an unexpected gift neatly packaged in delicate wrappings and frustratingly tagged, 'Do not open till Christmas.' " In an ever-so-light touch his fingertips traced the shapely curve of her calf and then slowly trailed upward to the frilly lace cresting above her dimpled knee.

"Do you tell all your lady visitors such nice things, Mitch?" Her dark eyes fell upon the shadowed angles of his upturned face.

"You're the first lone lady visitor who's ever been invited into this abode. I'm a very discriminating person. One who'd rather do without than settle for anything less than what I want." Like the soft, flickering glow of firelight, his expressive eyes attracted and held hers. "And from the first moment we met, I wanted you!"

Deliberately his hand deserted the streamlined leg for the silken strands of her hair, slipping amid the wispy curls with a gentle, persuasive tug that pulled her lips to his. At first their mouths barely touched, gliding airily on gossamer wings. Then, languidly, his lips teased hers in soft, brushing strokes, seducing, torturing, until finally and firmly kissing her with the absolute power that only mutual ardor gives.

Natural repositioning came in sensual moves—his hand running down her slim throat, over a tensed shoulder, massaging through the sheer material until all tenseness vanished. Inevitably she followed his guiding weight to the support of the fluffy pillow, her hair spilling in a golden fan upon the velvety blue.

For a motionless, communicative second Mitch's adoring gaze held hers. Then, with expressive tenderness, his fingertips combed through her gold-spun hair in a drugging, nearly hypnotic motion.

There was a compulsiveness about the moment—a dreamy, out-of-control quality. It was as if all sense of time and touch had become greatly exaggerated and indescribably poignant.

With fragile, malingering kisses Mitch traveled her face. From temple to temple, from her forehead to her chin, along the delicate curve of her jawline to the touchy indent at the base of each ear, he slowly . . . sensitively . . . made love to her. The subtleness of his lovemaking became a catalyst which sparked the latent passion lurking within Del.

Her breath caught as, unconsciously, her palms clasped the nape of his neck to guide the sensual meander of his lips along the alive length of her throat. The swell of her breasts as she, at last, drew a breath provocatively outlined the perfect symmetry of her bust. As naturally as her next intake of air Mitch's hand cupped her supple curves, savoring the excited expansion of their soft fullness beneath his seductive touch.

Deftly his free hand unfastened the first few buttons of her blouse. Then, easing back the sheer material, he nestled a cheek against the fleshy cleavage that crested above her French-cut bra. A betraying tremor encompassed Del's hand as it lighted upon his dark hair and began a melding stroke of the rich strands. Swathed in a timeless, wordless utopia, Mitch pressed his warm lips to her pounding heart.

"Del . . ." His incoherent whisper became lost in a maze

of mutual emotion. Even he did not realize that the uttering of her name was both an endearment and a question. Her answering sigh brought his mouth upon hers in a prolonged, cherishing kiss.

Fevered and primed, his muscular length lay against her sleek one. A conflict of aching restraint and intense desire clouded his hungry gaze. Even through the bulk of clothing, her perfection was apparent and seductive.

"Lovely," he whispered. "I wonder how perfect you actually are." His lips caressed her throat, the rapid race of the pulsebeat at the hollow of her neck igniting his adrenaline. God! How he wanted to feel the texture of that skin—to run his palm over every inch of femininely scented flesh. He had never wanted a woman in the way he wanted her—not merely physically but soulfully, selfishly, completely.

He glanced at her fair face—eyes closed, thick fringed lashes casting shadows on flushed cheeks, narrow-bridged nose, dainty and aloof, full, inviting mouth that obliterated a man's restraint. She was more than lovely. She was guileless, and fresh, and solitary—everything, anything a man could ever wish for.

Again he claimed those tempting lips—those warm, moist, memorable lips that haunted his dreams and stalked his waking thoughts. He knew that possession was nine-tenths of the law, and nine-tenths of him belonged to the honey-haired sorceress whose kiss either cursed or graced him, whichever fate decreed.

Reluctantly he released her mouth. In the firelight's reflection he caught the shimmer of a tear trailing from the corner of her eye. Stunned, he brushed her cheek with the back of his hand as he staved off the physical demands his body begged to satisfy.

"Del, honey . . ." She turned her head from his amatory gaze and imploring tone. Unable to finish because he didn't know what to say, he tenderly wiped away the traces of her despair.

"Oh, Mitch, I want you. Believe me, I do. It's so hard to explain. When I lose control of my emotions, I freeze inside. I try to overcome the panic, but I can't. I just can't." The inflection in her voice defined "can't."

"Forgive me," she begged, closing her eyes as if to block out a threatening menace.

Taking great pains to avoid misinterpretation, Mitch eased himself nearer, wincing at the uncontrollable shudder he felt pass through her body. "Forgive you?" he said soothingly, gently brushing the tumbled tresses from her tensed face. "I'm the one who's rushing things." He paused, a pensive furrow creasing his forehead. "Who am I kidding? I'm racing!"

Strong arms enfolded her, as if by sheer physical superiority he could bond her to him. "I'm not asking what stands between us, Del . . . at least not now. All I really want is to hold you. Believe it or not, I need to embrace a believer." His reassuring hand caressed the side of her face. "The night's young, the fire warm, and our needs complicated and great. For now can't we just lie together? Can't we just talk and share this moment, one caring person holding another."

The words were stirring, his touch compelling, and as she gazed up into his sincere eyes, for the first time in her life she felt a strong urge to put her faith in a man.

The cedar crackled to a Bach sonata, while cast against the shimmering firelight, two bronzed silhouettes hesitantly came together in a gentle embrace. As she lay snuggled with her head on Mitch's broad shoulder, the smallest of details became momentous to Del—the feel of cashmere, soft; the thudding of his heart, strong. And just as probable as the morning sunrise, she knew their time would come.

CHAPTER FOUR

The wind blew stout, advancing bleak clouds across fall skies while stirring a dusty haze over the open target range. Like the dissonant weather, the mood of the assembled officers deteriorated as the annual qualifying session dragged on.

Even Deeder seemed strangely subdued as he preceded Del to the mark. Taking a firm grip on the butt of his snub-nosed revolver, he drew a steady bead on the shadowed "kill area" of the practice target. Barely had the first syllable of the commence order been given when the Colt cleared the holster. Successively it fired in split-second intervals.

Blast after volatile blast, the pent-up frustration in Deeder exploded, his concentration almost tangible, yet his final shot as impotently misdirected as his anger. With a disgusted shrug the pro emptied the carboned hulls upon the dried clay. Then, after reloading, he silently turned and paced off the distance to the twenty-five-yard line.

Del drew her pistol and took her turn at the firing line, then moved to take her place behind Deeder at the next qualifying mark.

News traveled fast around the cop shop. Every officer present had heard of yesterday's defeat on the drug case and, to the man, resented the absurd hypocrisy of it all. After that debacle the seeming futility of their battle against the judicial system rankled deeply. For if, by some miracle, a cop managed to break the preliminary entanglements that tied his hands, in the end the rights of the accused, bureaucratic red tape, or the intervention of do-good liberals would bind his efforts.

She looked down the line of twelve men on the mark, revolvers aimed, feet astraddle to steady their shots, and jaws tightly clamped in determination. One characteristic ran through all—sullen frustration. Who cared if they lost another case? What did it matter if once again a guilty-as-sin defendant walked away, acquitted and smirking? After all, what was one more defeat? Del's silent reply came as reflexively as the sigh she breathed for them: They cared; she cared! The range officer's command broke into her swirling thoughts.

"Ready on the right . . . ready on the left . . . ready on the line . . . commence firing!" A volley of bitter bullets ripped into the papier-mâché target, riddling the symbol of their united anger. How many of them visualized Mitchell Parrish? If not his actual features, the hazy outline of all he represented? With murderous accuracy the cracking shots hit the kill area over and over, the acrid smell of gunpowder diluted in the open air, but pungent in Del's mind.

She was as torn as the mangled target, her troubled heart as pierced as the black-outlined silhouette. That part of Mitchell Parrish assaulted by the outpouring of copper-jacketed wrath she hated as much as they did. But would they ever know the tender, compassionate man she'd come to discover? No . . . one look at their faces was answer enough. If her fellow officers ever learned of her association with Mitch, all she'd striven so long to gain would be undone. They wouldn't accept or understand her relationship with the despised counselor. No, all they would see would be a frivolous feminine traitor!

Snapping closed her down-lined vest, Del strode to the line, planted her boots an exacting distance apart, and straight-armed her Chief's Special. The chilling wind blowing across the open field tossed her wild curls back from her tense face as the range officer's command intermingled with the gusting whine.

"Ready on the right . . ." his voice droned. Del zeroed in on the target, her heart pounding and her mind playing tricks. How had she become involved with a man who could easily destroy what little recognition she'd struggled so hard to achieve? Why'd he have to be unforgettably good-looking? The approaches of so many men over the past years had left her cold, untouched. Why did this man have to affect her so powerfully, so deeply?

"Ready on the left . . ." Del took a deep breath, fighting for concentration, but obstinately her mind refused. The right-left analogy thrashed in her head. Weren't she and Mitch always right and left of every issue with only one exception—their compelling physical attraction for each other? Oh, why'd it have to be him?

"Ready on the line . . ." Her extended arm grew taut as she realized the gravity of what she'd been doing—putting her professional life on the line for her private one. Why should she take such a reckless gamble? Because he was the first man in years who'd exposed the sensitive needs she'd long ago buried deep inside, the first to make her feel alive and, for a precious moment, unafraid of being a woman? God! Why'd it have to be him?

"Commence firing!" Like that of her male comrades, Del's jawline tightened as her finger squeezed the trigger, annihilating the paper adversary looming in the distance. Mechanically she fired again and again until the dull click of an empty chamber recalled her to the present. Then, with a practiced flip of the cylinder, she ejected the spent cartridges at her feet. For a long, numb moment she stared down at the gutted shells until Deeder's familiar drawl revived her from the chill of iced reflection.

"Been practicin', or did ya wake up just plain mean today?" the proud tutor said, joshing her. Raising her dazed eyes, she collided with his paternal grin.

"Maybe a little of both," she replied blandly, forcing a faint smile while holstering her gun in the shoulder strap.

"Or maybe Annie Oakley struck out last night and is merely relievin' herself of a personal grudge?" They turned to face an eavesdropping Horton, standing a few feet away and grinning like a Cheshire cat.

"Which are ya jealous of, Horton—her outqualifyin' ya on the range or never gittin' the chance to pitch in her ball park?" Though Deeder's voice held its usual good-natured tone, his level gaze called Horton down. With a meaningful nod toward the parked sedan, he pointedly excused Del from the private lesson Horton was about to receive. Even in her tormented state of mind, she didn't envy Horton his predicament. Deeder could be a hard taskmaster when provoked.

Her snakeskin boots trudged across the sod field toward the car, the stark reality of her dilemma taking precedence in her thoughts. Oh, why, of all the men in the world to select from, had her heart chosen the controversial Mitchell Parrish?

Del slung open the car door and dropped to the seat. Moodily she gazed out across the open field as her mind harped on a selfish yet major consideration—her jeopardizing association with Mitchell Parrish.

Chancing the displeasure of her peers was one thing; risking a promotion by irritating her superiors was quite another. Though civil service law supposedly protected her from personal malice, she knew very well that a candidate could lose an edge by a subtle but powerful maneuver. All it took was for one vexed and vindictive superior to lower an efficiency rating. Since the performance evaluation was added to, and became part of, the overall test score, a few marginal points either way could make the difference between placing first or second. There was only one opening for the lieutenant's position, only one chance to make it.

Del closed her eyes and, for the umpteenth time, visualized the posted results. For months she'd reinforced herself by mentally picturing *her* name in black, bold letters at the top of the promotion list. She did it when tired from studying endless hours, when disheartened because petty prejudices forced her to prove herself again and again. Deep down, she knew that few of her fellow officers truly accepted her as an equal, most of their wives resented her, and all the superiors patronized their token female. Her personal struggles meant little to them; this small victory, everything to her. Though Mitch might very well help her realize her full potential as a woman, he could also cause her forfeiture of a dream.

Del's eyelids squeezed tighter, as if to block out the bluntness of her thoughts. Her arguments against Mitch sounded so calculated and unfeeling. But in the light of cold reality, weren't they accurate? Wasn't it necessary for her to face them now, full on, before she allowed this relationship to go any farther? Balancing the emotional tightrope she walked was becoming more difficult by the day. The more she exposed herself to Mitchell Parrish the man, the greater his appeal; the more to Mitchell Parrish the counselor, the greater her jeopardy.

Hearing Deeder's laugh in the distance, Del's eyes flicked open with a sudden tenseness. Only one thought kept her company as she waited: *Heaven help her! Why'd it have to be him?*

* * *

Eight hours later, as they cruised up I 10 in Mitch's plush Winnebago, the same plaguing questions drummed in Del's head. Sullenly she gazed out the window, suppressing an irrational urge to demand of him the answers which remained inexplicable to her. *How have we become as involved as we are?* she wanted to scream. Instead, she swallowed hard and continued to stare out onto the black nothingness of the open highway.

She didn't know whom she was more upset with: Mitch for imposing this minitrip upon her or herself for allowing him the liberty. For no sooner had she returned to the office when Deeder informed her she had a call on line two. Both surprise and dread filled her at the sound of Mitch's "hello." Momentarily stunned, she sank to her chair, maintaining the presence of mind to swivel away from Deeder's prying eyes. Then, rallying her senses about herself, she managed a meek greeting.

"I can barely hear you," Mitch had said. "I think we must have a bad connection."

"No," she replied as loudly as she dared. "I have a bit of a sore throat, is all." She peeked over her shoulder, pretending a scan of her desk. It was then that Lorraine, the buxom records clerk, made an opportune entrance. From past observation, Del knew that she would be good for at least a few minutes of distraction.

"I'm a little pressed at the moment," she said hurriedly. "Is there something in particular that you want?"

"Yes, there is," he answered with mock civility. "I called to see if you could arrange to take tomorrow and Friday off. What I had in mind was a camp-out along the Guadalupe. It's beautiful up in the hill country this time of year, and I wanted to introduce you to my second most favorite sport—rapid riding."

An instantaneous throbbing began at her temples.

Lightly she rubbed the psychosomatic ache with her fingertips while trying to think of a gracious yet expedient way to decline.

"I'm sorry, ah." She paused, glancing nervously about before softly adding his name. "I'm afraid it would be impossible for me to get away for a long weekend right now. Maybe we could do it another time?" At the sound of Lorraine's parting giggles she froze inside.

"Not good enough, Sergeant. We both know you're not so indispensable that the department couldn't function without you for a few days. I refuse to take no for an answer. In fact, I think I'll just wait on the line until you decide to say yes."

The throb grew worse as the tense pressure increased. Honestly! Sometimes she believed he was psychic. She sensed he could visualize her awkward circumstances and deliberately pressed the advantage. Aware that her privacy would be invaded at any moment, Del tried to appease him by postponing the issue.

"I'll try, but I can't promise. Now I really do have to get back. Call me at home this evening," she said, hedging, squirming in her chair.

"I'll do better than that. I'll be out front of your place at precisely seven o'clock. Bring old jeans, warm clothes, and don't forget heavy socks. I'll take care of everything else. And, Del?"

"Yes." She sighed.

"I'm sure if you begin to doctor that sore throat diligently, you'll make a miraculous recovery by tonight. Bye!" Immediately the connection went dead on his end.

With a frustrated bang Del hung up, turned back to her desk, and placed her throbbing head between her hands for a moment.

"Trouble?" Deeder's bulky figure blocked her preoccupied view.

"Ah, no!" She instantly perked up, reaching for a complaint form buried beneath a stack of folders. "I just need to see about taking a couple of days comp time. A friend and I are considering a four-day camping trip up into the hill country." She tried to keep her face blank, her voice nonchalant.

"Sounds like a good deal to me. Your friend male or female?" The laugh lines etching the corners of Deeder's teasing eyes cut deeper.

"And what difference does that make?" Del said challengingly.

"Oh, not much, I guess. 'Ceptin' the nights get mighty cold around this time of year, and snugglin's a far sight better when ya cozy up to a man."

"Deed, do me a favor?" Steady brown eyes locked upon his tickled features.

"Sure thing, Del."

"Quit worrying over my sleeping arrangements. I'm perfectly capable of handling them myself."

"That a fact? Well, 'pears to me you ain't been doin' such a bang-up job, hot dog. Course, it's your business, but I kin tell ya for sure ya'd sleep a whole lot more contented with a man beside ya." Satisfied with having had his say, Deeder had shot her a playful wink before moseying off toward his own territory.

Later, on her way to the camping expedition with the male sleeping partner Deeder so strongly endorsed, she was both excited and angered: excited at the prospect of being with Mitch again; angered by his easy manipulation of her.

She focused on the copper moon majestically illuminating the hill country's rolling terrain. Somehow its opaqueness seemed symbolic of her undefined and unexpressed feelings for Mitch. Ever since picking her up, he'd been pleasant and companionable while she'd been sulky and shrewish. It was no wonder he'd wisely withdrawn from her double-edged responses and occupied himself with the drive.

Things certainly hadn't gotten off to a good start, but she'd be darned if she'd take all the blame. What right did he have to be so decisive, presumptuous, and possessive? Was he so sure of himself? Or was it that he was so sure of her?

The motor home turned onto a winding side road that trailed toward the riverbank. The steep curves became treacherous, the mammoth oaks arching overhead creating an eerie weave of night shadows. Maybe he was a modern-day Pied Piper, she mused. And just as in the fairy tale, his mesmerizing power would lead her away to oblivion. It certainly seemed so. For didn't she always succumb to his wishes and, like a submissive child, follow?

An arched entrance appeared up ahead, the words "River's Edge Campsite" inscribed above. The Winnebago forged on through, and Mitch idled up to the farthest, most secluded end of the park before shutting off the engine.

"Here we are!" he said in the asinine way people often do when the apparentness of the fact is quite obvious.

"So I see," she replied in the same singsong voice, deliberately emphasizing the absurdity of his statement.

Mitch slanted a look in her direction. She glanced away. The small front quarters of the vehicle became stifled.

"Well," he drawled, "I guess we'd better get the power hooked up and settle down for the night." Even in the darkened confines he noted the reflexive stiffening of her body.

"Just sit tight while I check in. I won't be long," he assured her, grabbing his leather jacket and springing from the Winnebago with an exaggerated slam of the door.

Involuntarily she flinched, cursing beneath her breath at her frayed nerves, which were as brittle as the rustle of fallen leaves beneath Mitch's boots.

In a few minutes the power came on, and a welcome flood of light filtered from the back portion of the motor home. Del slowly eased her way to the roomy kitchen area directly behind and stretched her cramped legs.

"All the comforts of home," she muttered sarcastically, trailing a hand over one compact appliance after another as her eyes followed a path of serviceable indoor-outdoor carpeting leading aft to a small bath and . . . beyond . . . a door, behind which she knew were the sleeping quarters.

She stood immobile, mentally paralyzed at the sight of the ominous bedroom. A clammy sheath enveloped her recoiling flesh, and her pulse dropped to a deathlike rate.

"Everything's secured. All we need to do is batten down the hatches and get some rest." Mitch's voice spanned the twilight zone that lay between the reality of now and the memories of a scarred past. "We'll have wasted the whole trip if we miss sunrise on the river. It's almost as breathtaking as the white water ride." His incessant drone beckoned her attention. Slowly her gaze released itself from the looming portal, drawn in the direction of his distracting voice.

"I brought along some imported beer. Would you care for a nightcap?" Mitch continued, leaning within the small refrigerator. A recognizable clink of glass bottles accompanied his words.

"Ah, no," she replied in a vague tone, her eyes unwillingly returning to the dreaded darkened quarters and visualizing the contents within: a massive bed, covers laid back, cold sheets bared, and two downy pillows side by side. Panic-stricken, she cringed from the vivid mental portrait, turning away with an abrupt "On second thought, yes."

Midway in the process of opening his draft, Mitch gazed puzzedly at her across the short distance. "Which is it, Del, yes or no?" he asked. Though his voice was calm, his intense eyes sought more than just a yea or nay response.

"Yes," she replied with a degree more conviction. With a patronizing shake of his head he retrieved the second bottle and proceeded to open both.

While watching his fluid male approach, Del subconsciously noted each lithe motion, every masculine detail. Yet consciously she rejected the nameless emotion that he stirred within her. He handed her the brown glass bottle, then motioned for her to sit. Flipping her blond curls petulantly, she all but snatched the iced brew from his hand and took a long much-needed gulp.

"What's with you tonight, Del?" Mitch slouched upon one of the couches, stretching out his long legs while studying her from beneath veiled lids.

"What do you mean?" she countered defensively, dropping to the opposite couch in an exaggerated flounce.

"Okay, I'll spell it out for you, Sergeant." He paused, took a sip, then wedged the bottle between his muscular thighs. "You've been behaving like an ill-tempered banty rooster all the way up here, pecking and strutting with your tail feathers stuck up in the air. I've been thinking on it real hard, and I'll be darned if I can recall having offended you. So if it's not me, it's got to be you."

His remarks served like a shot of adrenaline, a charge of reviving fury surging through her. Mimicking his pull on the long neck, she squared her shoulders and faced him with an impaling look.

"How very tidy of you, Counselor, to absolve yourself from all fault," she said tauntingly. "Maybe if I describe your pressure tactics in legal terms, you'll understand why I'm upset. When one is coerced into a situation not of her choice or making, I believe it's called entrapment. I'm sure you've programmed yourself to think that any woman would jump at the chance to be at your beck and call, but it so happens that I don't fit the mold. I don't like being manipulated, Mitchell Parrish, nor do I care very much for self-indulgent males!"

The words tumbled from her without forethought, her anxiety releasing itself in the only form it could take—lashing out at the nearest excuse.

Mitch's eyes tempered to cold steel, several strained moments passing before he finally spoke.

"I see, so your wretched mood is all due to my having the presumptuous gall to invite you camping. How inconsiderate of me!" He stood, walked a few paces, then turned and leveled an ashen gaze at her that harbored no warmth or compassion.

"Do you want to know what I think is really rubbing you wrong, Miss Harris?"

"I'm sure you'd tell me even if I said no." She raised her chin defiantly.

"I don't think you function well in social situations. By that I mean, take away that shiny gold shield you wear, strip you of your rank, and what's left? A frightened female who becomes terrified at the prospect of having to deal with being a real woman. You can't tolerate the fragile framework of a man-woman relationship—the complex emotions and delicate balance of trust and vulnerability. To be perfectly blunt, Sergeant, you're running scared of involvement, no matter how superficial it is!"

His angular face grew more set with each truth he spoke. "I'm curious. What turns a soft, sensitive woman into an efficient, unfeeling machine? When did you give up your citizenship in the human race and become so inflexible that a four-day camp-out somehow threatens your secure little world?"

He took a step toward her, but the emptiness of the dark, brooding eyes engaging his froze him in his tracks.

"Please continue, Counselor. Surely, after that character assassination, your usual dispassionate summation is in order. For you see, until this very moment I hadn't realized that I . . ."

The words caught in her throat. She tried again. "Even if I could defend myself, I'm not sure I would. . . . Not tonight. I readily concede that I'm difficult. As for my reasons . . ." She paused indecisively, but then lowered her gaze and murmured resignedly, "I'll take the fifth."

The last was the hardest of all—to admit the guilt, yet be unable to disclose the extenuating circumstances. A heavy silence erected an insurmountable wall between them. Slowly she rose to her feet and began to take the endless walk toward the dreaded room at the end of the hall. All the while she hoped against hope that her unsteady limbs wouldn't fail her.

"Del . . ." Her name tumbled beseechingly from his lips.

With a hesitant pause she turned to face the silent entreaty in his stare.

"We've got to stop doing this to one another—aiming for professional sore spots whenever we want to needle each other. God knows it's effective, but is it fair?"

She pondered his rationale for a moment, pinpointing the instances when each had been guilty of the tactic. Though the conflict was very real and the ammunition ample, was the cause worth the pain they inflicted? And yet . . . there was a nagging question about the character of her enemy that had to be laid to rest before she could arbitrate a truce—one minor concession on his part; one major misgiving on hers.

"Not only is it unfair, Mitch"—she sighed—"but it's

cowardly and cruel." She clung to his eyes as she cleaved to an intuition. "One weighty and necessary question, Counselor. Then we'll set aside our professional differences by mutual consent."

He nodded in acquiescence to her appeal.

"The Sanchez cocaine case, your later explanation about the sensationalistic tactic's being merely a means by which to draw attention to a fallacy within the law—were you sincere?"

Though his facial expression registered shock, there was also an element of naked conviction as he replied evenly and without hesitation, "Most sincere. That case was particularly distasteful to me. Though I'm obliged to render a capable defense, I'm not so amoral as not to hope that some shred of justice may be served."

A flood of sweet victory washed over her. "Our harassment of one another is over. In your words, the final arguments have been heard; in mine, case closed." She cocked her head, half smiled, and then turned toward the bedroom door.

"About my earlier accusation and your taking the fifth . . ." He faltered, recapturing her attention. "Any judgment can be appealed," came the softly spoken apology.

She stopped, hung her head thoughtfully, and then glanced back in his direction. "Since it's been a long, hard day and the accused is very tired, she enters a plea of nolo contendere. Good night, Mitch." A melancholy smile flitted across her vixen lips a moment before she crossed over the symbolic threshold. With a soft click the sliding door closed.

Dejectedly a pair of blue-gray eyes continued to stare into the empty space where, seconds ago, a desirable yet untouchable woman had stood. The irises grew moodily dark as the solitary figure pondered her parting Latin phrase—nolo contendere: no contest.

CHAPTER FIVE

The first golden slivers of dawn stretched above the towering bluffs, rays of mellow sunlight filtering through the spindling pines and prisming on the docile river's surface. The air had a crisp, dewy quality that made one feel reincarnated, and the only sounds that broke the early-morning stillness were the chirps of winter sparrows mingled with the rhythmic lap of the Guadalupe as it flowed its archaic course.

As Del sat huddled upon a flat boulder at the river's edge, sipping coffee and trying to emerge from a sleepless night's stupor, it seemed to her as if the rest of the world had declined to answer the daily summons to existence. For here on the riverbank, bundled up from her knit-capped head to her rubber-booted toes, she felt removed from humanity in general. The loner within her loved the special feeling and openly resented Mitch's intrusion on such sacred moments of privacy. Not only was he noisy while hovering over his precious equipment and raft, but his constant interruptions with requests for her help were tediously annoying.

For Pete's sake! He must think he's about to explore the uncharted Amazon the way he fusses. She griped beneath her breath, wincing at yet another of his grating summonses.

With a perturbed sigh she flung out what little coffee she had left and then lumbered in the cumbersome boots to Mitch's side.

"We're just about ready to shove off. Here, put this on." He held out a gaudy orange life jacket in her direction.

"I can't move for all the clothes I have on now," she complained. "Can't I just keep it next to me in the boat?"

"I told you before—it isn't a boat. It's a raft, and no, you can't. The preserver's a precautionary measure for your own protection. What if you were to spill into the rapids? It's not like calm waters. The best of swimmers have been known to go under," Mitch explained, trying to hide his impatience with her adolescent remarks.

He'd spent a rotten night, cramped on his half of the bed and plagued by disappointing and frustrating thoughts. His disposition matched his physical condition—rumpled and ornery.

"You do swim, don't you?" He stopped in mid-zip of his own preserver, glancing into the blank toffee eyes that gave him his answer. "Terrific! And you don't want to wear the jacket. Put it on and leave it on!"

Grudgingly Del complied, struggling with the bulky thing until her exasperation forced Mitch to lend a hand. After a final zip he tweaked her stubborn chin. "There, all snug. Now for a crash course in the art of rapid riding." He reached for one of the oars and then smiled condescendingly.

"This is what we commonly refer to as an oar. Contrary to popular belief, it is not an accent piece to complement the inner raft, nor is it a gigantic back scratcher. What it is is an instrument by which we will propel ourselves through calm waters and navigate the white."

Del's dark eyes flashed. If she were conducting a most

irritating boor of the week contest, he'd win by a landslide! "Do go on, Counselor. I find your witty lecturing most enlightening," she said flippantly, crossing her arms over her chest and tapping a loppy boot.

"Pay close attention, Sergeant. You might learn something by sheer accident," he countered with a roguish grin. "When we hit the white water, which in layman's terms means the rough, swirly stuff, we must hit it head-on. That means that we both, I repeat, *both,* paddle for all we're worth and try to keep the raft on a straight course. *Comprende?*"

A curt nod of her head bounced the tassel atop her knit cap impertinently.

"Good! Then, since you're such a quick study, we'll move along to the next phase. I'll be taking the point—the front of the raft—in order to be lookout and navigator. That leaves you the job of helmsman. Simply put, your primary function is to turn us whenever it becomes necessary to evade things like boulders, low-hanging tree branches, or other river obstacles. Ruddering is as easy as pie. All you have to do is hold your paddle flat and firm against the onrush of water on either the right or left side, whichever direction I tell you turn. Like so!" He demonstrated the position. "You think you can handle that?"

He knew very well that the job of helmsman should go to the stronger and more seasoned rafter, but he couldn't resist an opportunity to intimidate, as well as initiate, Miss Haughtiness.

"Since I'm the only candidate for the position, I hardly think the question's relevant, Counselor," Del snapped testily.

"A point well taken, Sergeant." He grinned, seemingly oblivious to her barbs. "Okay, well, I guess that just about covers it. Remember, no dangling your legs over the edge, feet inside the raft at all times. First white water we come to will be Slumber Falls. There's about a three-foot drop, so don't get flustered. The tricky part comes right after. Stay alert and rudder when I say, and you'll take it like a pro." He smiled winningly.

Del found it infuriating that he could be equally as handsome in a turtleneck beneath a rough outing shirt and Wranglers, as he could in the latest three-piece Halston and a pair of $500 Anaconda boots. His quizzical gaze roused her, and she realized she'd been out and out staring at him. Quickly she diverted the embarrassing emphasis.

"Is drinking coffee while canoeing permissible, Captain Bligh, or is that considered mutinous?" she gibed, refusing his hand as she stepped into the awkwardly pliant raft.

"We're not going canoeing, Del." His hand ran through his ebony hair in an exasperated motion. "As for coffee breaks, use your own discretion."

Mitch gave a mighty push, and the raft surged ahead. Del bounced from her rubber perch on the edge, sprawling among the gear in the bottom as Mitch leaped on board.

"Paddle out toward center, and then we'll head downstream," Mitch commanded, oblivious to her plight as he took the point.

Hampered by the cumbersome clothes and unsure footing, she huffed her way back up to the tufted edge of the raft, clinging tight as it made its cumbrous way crosscurrent. At last, beginning to acclimate to the buoyancy, she decided that she'd better pitch in and paddle before Mitch discovered her freeloading in the rear. The oar felt clumsy in her hands; her first dip into the water, less than dexterous. It became a battle of wills—hers against the stubborn wooden object. It turned in her hand, flipped about like a floundering fish in the water, and once almost completely slipped from her hold.

"What are you doing back there?" Mitch shouted, peering back to check her progress. "We're fighting each other, Del. Go to the opposite side, right arm extended, and then dip smooth and easy." He exaggerated his stroke in order to demonstrate the move.

Del repeated the procedure, first to the left, then to the right, mumbling with each switch, "Smooth and easy . . . smooth and easy," in a mocking tone. If Mitch heard, he paid no heed, continuing to work his way methodically toward the middle of the river.

"Okay, Del, now left rudder while I paddle, and we'll turn 'er about."

Immediately Del's mind went blank. She'd completely forgotten how to left rudder. In fact, she was so befuddled she couldn't even remember which way was left.

"Come on, girl, left rudder . . . left rudder!" Captain Bligh was yelling.

At last the word "left" made an impression, and Del dropped her oar into the water in the pretense of ruddering. By some divine intervention whatever she'd done had been correct. For suddenly the raft began to rotate to the left. The only problem was that it kept on swerving, and before she knew it, they were facing the bank from which they'd just embarked.

"Right rudder!" came the reversed order. "Right . . . right!"

A deep scowl furrowed Del's forehead as she swung the oar to the right. "You don't have to shout, Mitchell Parrish. I'm not hard of hearing!"

A shrug of his broad shoulders was the only satisfaction she received. As if to add insult to injury, the obstinate Guadalupe waters repelled the oar with a plopping slap. How on earth was she supposed to right rudder when she didn't even know how to left rudder?

"Enough . . . draw up." Mitch stroked at a furious pace until finally he had them back on course and traveling downstream with the swift current.

Del rubbed her already aching forearms with a grimace. "You'll have to carry on without your rudderman for a few minutes because she's taking a well-earned coffee break." Her tone practically dared him to take issue.

"Go ahead, but make it snappy. Slumber Falls is only a half mile up ahead."

"Aye, aye, sir!" she quipped, a glimmer of a smile breaking her rosy-cheeked face for the first time.

Pouring coffee from a Thermos while roller-coastering downstream was no task for the fainthearted. The only thing that took more fortitude was synchronizing the cup with one's mouth while bobbing like a cork upon the water. It wasn't easy, but Del's persistence won out. After what seemed like forever, she felt the warmth of the aromatic brew slip past her gullet. A long sigh escaped her as she silently congratulated herself on her adeptness while pausing to take in the landscape.

The setting was breathtaking: imposing bluffs rising vertically from the river's edge were densely covered in autumn-leafed oaks, evergreen pines, and fragile sweet gums. Between them, the clear, swift waters of the Guadalupe weaved a course through smooth granite boulders and overhanging cypress trees. High above, the golden sun displayed its fully risen splendor against a cloudless indigo sky. The panorama stretched endlessly, while they, like Tom Sawyer and Huck Finn, drifted toward the adventures that it held in store for them.

Actually the ride was very pleasant. It was the raft's cantankerous captain who spoiled the serenity with his "do this," "do that," better-than-thou attitude. Maybe if she made an effort to be more congenial, he'd reciprocate in kind, she thought. At least it was worth a try. So, with the casual civility of a passenger on a Mediterranean cruise, Del made a halfhearted attempt to be social.

"How cold would you say the water is, Mitch?"

"About forty degrees. Why? Are you thinking of abandoning ship?" A goading grin broke his face as he glanced back at her. "I wouldn't if I were you. You'll go numb after ten seconds in that water."

"I assure you I wasn't contemplating it. I was only curious, is all." So much for congeniality. She pouted, sipping the last of the coffee and replacing the lid.

"Stow the coffee, Del. Slumber Falls is just around the bend. Remember what I told you to do, and don't panic."

Unable to contain herself, Del wrinkled her nose at his back, scoffing aside his warning with a cool "I seldom panic, Counselor."

Another shrug was all she gained for her efforts. With a blasé air she secured the Thermos and made ready for the little dip that he'd overdramatized.

As the raft rounded the bend, Del's face blanched, and her fingers clenched the oar in a death grip. Ahead lay what Mitch had, minimally, described as the rough, swirly stuff. *There must be some mistake,* she thought. *We must have missed a turn.* A short distance away she could see the current intensify, roll over a sharp rock shelf, and then plummet into a frothy whirlpool of aquatic mania. Beyond was an obstacle course of gigantic boulders, spaced dangerously close, with frenzied water weaving between and crashing over them in thundering sprays.

They would soon reach the point of no return. Silently Del reiterated what, in retrospect, had to be her most ludicrous quote: "I seldom panic . . . I seldom panic." Her heart thudded in her throat. Only a few more feet until . . .

They toppled over the edge and plunged into the wildly thrashing waters below. Del's breath came as erratically as the waves against the raft. Foamy spray drenched her face and arms as wide-eyed, she watched Mitch battle for control. She knew she should help, but her rebellious limbs refused to comply. Del cringed as the raft crashed against a huge boulder. Mitch rammed his paddle against the rock, pushing them into yet another cyclone of white water.

The paddle lay lifeless within her hands. Mitch stroked like a madman in the attempt to guide them between another set of rocky impasses a few yards away.

"Right rudder, Del!" he bellowed above the roar.

Obeying seemed the only rational thing to do. She lowered her paddle, straining to hold it steady against the onslaught of gushing water.

"Hold her hard to the right. Good! Good! Now drag up."

Mitch tersely shouted orders as he expertly navigated the raft through the main turbulence and out onto calmer waters.

"Bet you've never experienced anything quite as thrilling, have you?" he asked in boyish exhilaration.

"Thrilling! Are you serious?" Del's stunned eyes turned back to the white water in disbelief. "Petrifying would be more like it. I think you harbor a secret death wish, Counselor."

"It's an unpredictable sport—every ride a new challenge, man against nature, so to speak. But the best part is that nothing is sacrificed to enjoy it. There's no kill involved."

"No kill! What if you lose the test and the rapids swallow you up?" she protested.

"So you take a little dunk. You can ride the length of this river in a preserver if you're agile. Oh, by the way, if you ever do go in and the rapids suck you under, just remember not to panic. Eventually you'll come up again. Worse thing to do is panic," he stressed, unaware that Del's blood had congealed throughout her system.

"Tactfully put, Counselor. I'll keep it in mind."

"Waco Falls is next on the agenda. If you thought Slumber was a kick, wait'll we take this. You'll love it!"

"I can hardly wait," she mumbled, noticing his silent eye command to paddle, paddle, paddle.

The Guadalupe was a curious entity. Del found herself touched by the mystique of the waterway, wondering what tales of joy, trials, courage, and indignities it had witnessed during its timeless journey. For it had been a part of history and would continue to flow its immortal course long after she, and the world as she knew it, ceased to exist.

"Waco!" Mitch whooped. "Brace yourself, and paddle like crazy. We got to hit it head-on."

She didn't have to be told twice. The oar plunged, propelled, then plunged again. This time she wouldn't be intimidated by the swirling mass ahead. This time she'd show Mitchell Parrish that she could handle herself every bit as well as he. The raft pitched upon the savage waters, Mitch and she fighting for balance and command as they surged ahead to meet the Guadalupe's defiance. Threatening boulders rose before them, but she ruddered while Mitch jammed and stroked through the jutted maze. The water inside the raft reached ankle-deep on Del's boots as yet another spray rained down upon their heads.

They skimmed and bobbed along, struggling to keep the raft from capsizing. Del could see calmer waters ahead, but a gnarled limb draped directly in their path.

"Right rudder!" Mitch yelled as he pointed out the immediate and menacing danger.

She held her arms taut, gave it everything she had. The raft pivoted, Mitch ducking in the nick of time and the limb missing his head by inches. She'd done it! But engrossed in her power play, she'd made a fatal mistake—forgetting to draw up. The raft made a semicircle, and suddenly Mitch had the rear, she the point, and they were taking the last of the falls backward. Teeth clenched, fingers dug into rubber, she rode out the rocking turbulence with death-defying determination.

Realizing Mitch's amused eyes were upon her, she forced a flimsy smile. "Personally I thought I did a pretty good job back there." She fished for a morsel of praise.

"Pretty good, but you need a bit more practice before we make another run at the Guadalupe. When you're seasoned, we'll take it in a canoe. That's *real* rapid riding!" His eyes deepened mischievously to blue.

More than a little piqued, she adjusted her knit cap with a haughty tug, then lifted her chin indignantly. Boy! Would she ever relish an opportunity to tell him where he could stow his Guadalupe until it seasoned!

Familiar with that stubborn set of her chin, Mitch returned to his rhythmic paddling, ignoring her miffed airs.

For several, excruciatingly quiet moments, they drifted with the current while Del offered only her profile. She could be an irritating little stinker when she wanted to, Mitch mused; glancing at the rebuffing, stubborn set of her neck and then back out at the water. Why was he so attracted to her? She was distant, competitive, and when angered, she could be downright abusive. So why did he continue to perpetuate their relationship? Because she was also beautiful, sensitive, and, at rare moments, almost attainable? The roar of rushing waters ahead drew his attention back to the river.

"Laredo Bridge is the cutoff point, Del. I had the park manager drive the Winnebago down earlier so we'd have transportation back. Laredo's different, so listen up." He paused purposefully, awaiting her acknowledgment of his presence. Finally, with a childlike pout, she turned and faced him.

"As we go over the drop, the water's the roughest yet, but more important, there are treacherous boulders that divide the course. To the left are dangerous low hangs that only canoes or kayaks can pass. We *must* go to the right. Then we cut to shore as soon as possible because the bridge is only two hundred yards ahead and only a couple of feet off the water's surface. Eight people have lost their lives careening into the bridge this year alone. Needless to say, it's going to be the most challenging part of the trip."

Del shrugged her shoulders nonchalantly. "Are you ready to change seats, Captain?"

"I think not. It might be in our best interests if I take over the helm for a while."

"Good strategy, Captain—more brawn than brains." She cocked her head, shooting him an impish smile. It gave her immense pleasure to put His Smugness in his place.

"I suggest you turn yourself around unless you want to go down in the *Guinness Book of World Records* as the only fool to take Laredo Falls backward!" came the cynical comeback.

With a flip of her head and a swish of her Wrangler'd tush, she about-faced, finding herself staring straight onto the wildly thrashing waters of Laredo Bridge. The ominous granite boulder divide that Mitch had referred to earlier loomed before her, and though she would never admit it, she was thankful for his hands upon the rudder. The moment of truth was descending upon them, and as she paddled, her head filled with crazy thoughts: What became of orphaned mama cats, and would she have passed the upcoming lieutenant's exam this spring? A flash of Deeder's shocked expression as he read a fatality report listing her as the river's latest victim while traveling with a male companion by the name of Mitchell Parrish superimposed itself on her mind. That alone was incentive enough to survive!

They were quickly approaching the drop. As the waters

began to churn and the roar boomed in her ears, a silent Hail Mary echoed in her head.

The raft plummeted over the ledge into a crest of frothy whitecaps and began to spin with their crazed suction. Panicked, she glanced over her shoulder to see Mitch holding right with every ounce of strength he possessed—muscled biceps distended, a grimace on his solemn face, and his whole body stiff with exertion. The raft obeyed its master, pulling out of the spin and clipping inches alongside the giant boulder divide.

Del exhaled with relief, but prematurely. Before them the low bridge grew closer and closer, and another boulder lay directly in their path. Reflexively she extended her paddle to ward off the impending crash as she had seen Mitch do previously.

"No, Del, don't try it!" Mitch boomed in warning as he concentrated on steering in an attempt to swerve clear of the imminent collision.

The splinter of wood went unheard above the roar of the rapids as the paddle broke on impact, knocking Del off-balance and sending her toppling into the chilled eddy below. The merciless waters spun her body as she flailed and grasped at the air as though searching for an invisible lifeline. Her mind was as numb as her limbs, a one-and-only thought repeating: *God! I can't swim!.*

Instantly Mitch reacted, leaping from the raft and waging a desperate fight against the mire of turbulent waters to reach her floundering body before it was carried beyond his help. It was a costly battle, time and his own exhaustion working against him. Only raw will drove him on until his groping hand felt the saturated sleeve of her flannel shirt. Obsessively he clung to her arm while, by sheer physical strength, he propelled them away from the oncoming bridge.

Once he had reached a point where he could stand, his

brawny arms slipped beneath her rag-doll figure, lifting her limp body from the crystal waters into his secure hold. Slowly he struggled toward the bank and then eased his rescued burden to the dry earth. Panting with exertion, his eyes hazed with concern, he fell to his knees and examined her. Though fully conscious, she bordered on shock. There was a deathlike pallor to her skin and a bluish hue upon her lips as she lay drained and coughing, spasmodic shivers running the length of her body. Between his heaving gasps, Mitch's fear vented itself in impulsive anger.

"Damn fool stunt, Del. You could have gotten us both killed!" he growled.

"I only did the same as you," she managed breathlessly.

"You're hardly experienced enough to follow my act. I guess you think you can wear my pants, too," he ranted, half-crazy with thoughts of what might have happened.

"One sure thing, Counselor, I wouldn't pull 'em on any different!" Under the shock of his brash and unfair attack, her own ire exploded.

"Come on, woman. We can't lie out here freezing to death. Let's get inside before we both have pneumonia." With a rough handclasp he jerked her to her feet, then looked back out onto the rapids in time to see the deserted raft drift under the bridge and glide on down river.

"Terrific! You're an expensive weekend, Miss Harris. I'll give you that!"

"And you're a tyrannical boor. I can't remember when I've had a more miserable time!" she spat, stomping off with an emphatic squish of her boots. Seconds later her furious slam of the Winnebago's door left it rattling on its hinges.

"The woman could tear up a ball bearing," he fumed, matching her furious gait toward the motor home and then following through with a slam of his own.

Grabbing a bottle of brandy from the closet, he dripped

a second wet trail along the hallway to the bedroom. The atmosphere within the small room became electric upon his entrance. Like mortal adversaries, they glared across the neutral space between them, each daring the other to advance.

CHAPTER SIX

"Strip out of those wet clothes and get under the covers!" Mitch demanded, turning his back on her. With an angry slam of the brandy bottle to the nightstand, he began to peel off his own drenched shirt.

Beneath the bedraggled curls clinging to her forehead Del's eyes grew terrorized as she watched his undressing moves. Evasively she began to retreat around the end of the bed. "The hell I will!" she rasped as her rigid back met a walled obstruction.

Mitch spun in her direction, his patience stretched its limit and his ignited temper out of control. Unceremoniously his shirt fell in a heap upon the floor an instant before he approached with a lithe, deliberate stride. Del's eyes darted to the doorway calculatingly, but Mitch's oncoming figure blocked her only route of escape. Helplessly she found herself peering into detached, cool gray eyes that belied the smoldering rage about to explode.

"The hell if you won't!" The words struck simultaneously with his rendering yank upon the front of her shirt. A scathing rip tore into her senses as the resistant material gave way and severed buttons ricocheted off the walls and floor.

With her stunned gasp, two perfectly sculptured, rose-peaked breasts rose before him, and for a costly moment he hesitated. At that vulnerable instant Del attacked—lethal nails lashing out at his face, her only warning a seething hiss of "You bastard!"

Lightning quick, he caught her wrist before it reached his cheek, then wrestled the frenzied wildcat to the bed.

She squirmed, kicked, and heaved; he countered, levered, and pinned, their muffled curses and exerting pants mingling with the strained squeak of bedsprings and charging the small room.

"Are you crazy? I'm not going to hurt you!" Mitch's breathless words penetrated the blinding red haze of spontaneous mania as, at last, his superior strength subdued her and he held her immobile on the bed.

She couldn't see his face—only the nightmarish shadow of a pain and humiliation that returned her to the past. It was no longer Mitch who lay atop her, his coarse chest hair grazing her tender breasts, his painful grip bruising her wrists, and his heavy body pushing her back against the sheets. No! He was the man who, whatever he promised, would hurt her. He lied. He *always* lied, and he *always* hurt her.

Tears welled in her eyes, flowed into her hair as she cowered from the face above and dispassionately surrendered. "It wouldn't be the first time," she murmured.

Suddenly the imprisoning weight lifted. Confident hands removed the tattered remnants of her shirt, then unsnapped her wet jeans and eased the clinging dampness from her paralyzed legs. She lay lifeless and shivering until the downy feel of a bedspread cocooned her inert body, and she found herself drawn against a source of warmth. A gentle, stroking motion tamed her wild curls. Submissively Del's eyes closed, her chest heaves slowing to a rhythmic pace and coinciding with the life-giving source next to her. A sense of lethargic security enveloped her as the suffocating red haze drifted away and was replaced by a contented, warm glow.

"Tell me, Del," a lulling voice coaxed. "Tell me what you meant by its not being the first time." The sincerity of Mitch's entreaty touched a chord within her, the shock of his physical assault and culmination of intense emotions triggering wounding remembrances with a fervor that could not be ignored. For once the need to lay down the heavy load became paramount.

"Years ago, at eighteen, I married a man by the name of Jason Yates. I was young, naïve, and so very much in love," she began in an estranged voice. "I dreamed of Camelot; but in reality Jason reigned over Dun and Bradstreet, and our castle was a two-story Tudor in the suburbs. More practical than romantic, but then, as I said, I was naïve and young."

She hesitated, never opening her eyes, and she drew a deep breath before continuing. Somehow it seemed easier to speak in terms of myths.

"The nightmare began on my wedding night—the child-woman going to her marital bed with idealistic expectations of a perfect union, but finding instead a poor substitute. You see, when it came to lovemaking, Jason's usual chivalrous charm eluded him. He became a different person, a stranger I shared a bed with. I wasn't his queen; I was his whore."

An uncontrollable shudder passed through Del's body. Mitch's arms enclosed her tighter, his mellow drawl prompting, "Go on, Del. Let's get it out in the open once and for all."

"I thought he'd take me in his arms and slowly seduce me in the way I'd always imagined. Instead, he made demands, and when in my naïveté I clumsily blundered, he became impatient and angry."

Unconsciously Del began to wipe her palms on the coverlet as if trying to erase an invisible stain.

"Jason preferred to take a woman on a whim: his whim with no regard for hers. Only a total submission of body and spirit alike pleased him." The strangely emotionless quality of her voice frightened Mitch most of all. "There were no words of love, no feeling. Nothing."

Del's eyes opened wide. She lay staring up at the ceiling, picturing hurtful reflections. Her body tensed beneath the covers. Mitch edged closer in an attempt to lend comfort for the hurt she so apparently reexperienced.

"I was a young woman in love; he was a man in heat. We performed an act of copulation—uncomplicated, degrading copulation. Or do I mean to say capitulation?" The words tumbled in an avalanche of emotion, the shattering truths burying both her and Mitch in an aftermath of mental debris.

" 'Animals copulate; people make love,' I told myself. I wanted . . . needed . . . so much more. But Jason's needs were basic—he only wanted me . . . again and again. No, that's not exactly true." She groaned, almost as if she'd discounted Mitch's presence entirely and were speaking only to herself. "He didn't really want *me,* only a reservoir of relief."

A choked sound burrowed deeper within her throat. "Can you imagine the effect he had on me? You see, it wasn't just the physical abuse. Jason crushed my dreams. More important, my pride," she explained in broken words.

"Shhh," Mitch said soothingly, pressing her pale face to the cradle of his neck. "We don't have to talk about it anymore."

"I do . . . I do," she murmured incoherently. Somehow, in her move toward him, the coverlet had slipped away, and nothing separated her soft, curvaceous body from his own. He dared not pull away, yet he dared not give way to the sensual feel that played havoc with the manly urges threatening to betray his desire. Gently he massaged the graceful curve of her back, willing his thoughts to remain neutral.

"How long did you endure this, ah, marriage?" he asked, barely managing to disguise his repulsed anger.

"A little over a month," she admitted dazedly. "Every day I lived with the fear of an every night repetition. It almost drove me insane. Outside the bedroom Jason was the epitome of an ideal husband. Then, at night, behind closed doors . . ." Her voice trailed off. She pressed her palms to her eyes for a moment, blotting out a recollection too painful to relive. Then, sighing deeply, she added resignedly, "The marriage dissolved, yet somehow, fifteen years later, I'm still haunted by the memories."

Del shifted her head restlessly. "The one thing I can't forgive Jason for is depriving me of feeling like a woman. He scarred me in a way I can't overcome, no matter how hard I try."

Misty brown eyes gazed up into Mitch's compassionate face as she whispered, "I truly wonder what it's like . . . to feel that specialness others seem to enjoy. I feel cheated . . . unwhole."

Compulsively Mitch's fingertips caressed the outline of her pained face. It was such a simple wish, not nearly as complex as his yearning to fulfill it. Their candid gazes collided, facets of empathy, devotion, and resolve sparking his. And as she absorbed the energy of his look, the warmth of his nearness, the tenderness in his touch, Del knew that deliverance was but a word, a touch away.

"I can't stand the emptiness anymore." The confession spilled from her lips of its own volition. Yet once spoken, the long-suppressed desire could not be denied.

"Make me feel something, Mitch. Take away this ache,

and make me whole," she whispered imploringly. "Please, Mitch, make love to me!" Her soft palms slid up and along the familiar planes of his face, easing him nearer to the tantalizing mouth which softly begged, "Please, please, pl—"

Her words stilled on contact, emphasizing all the more the tormented moan which attested to the conflict raging within Mitch. Reluctantly he drew back from the alluring texture of her submitting mouth. His eyes deepened to a fathomless shade of blue, his voice becoming hoarse and strained when uttering, "You're confused, Del. I'm afraid you'd regret the moment. God! If you only knew how much I want you, but . . ."

Her fingertips pressed to his struggling lips, curtailing the good-intentioned excuses. "The time or man was never more right. I need you now, Counselor. There'll be no change of venue." A calm smile fell across the sultry mouth that murmured the words, yet there remained an urgent gleam within the gypsy eyes.

Mitch couldn't have refused even if he had wanted to, and he truly didn't. Quickly he rose and stripped off his clothes. He returned to her side with the adolescent jitters of a first-time experience. He'd been with his share of women—from the hot-blooded Latin girls of his youth to the cool, worldly sophisticates of more recent times. Yet none so potently stirred him, or caused him to suffer such egocentric pangs about performance, as this woman.

Thoughtfully he ran a hand through the feathery maze of blond curls. Performance wasn't the issue, he mentally debated. No! What was about to take place was much more meaningful. He was the salve to heal her wounds, the man chosen to make right what another had undone.

Gently tripping kisses over her dainty forehead, he erased the anxiousness from her brow. She needed the sustenance of a pure, untainted intimacy—someone to guide her toward a womanly destiny which she so desperately wished to fulfill.

Adoringly his lips snuggled her temple and then glided along the linear sleekness of her neck. A throaty sigh escaped her at the velvety contact of his seductive kisses. Alternately he lingered, tempted, then postponed her responses. She lay very still as if enchanted by his attention. Suddenly his purpose became clear: to love this woman in the way he'd imagined ever since meeting her, forgetting manly tests, locker room secrets, and textbook technique. All he needed to do was let go and allow his emotions, his commitment to carry them wherever love's fortune should lead.

Tenuously his large palms moved to her supple breast. He felt her tense, but with a light, caressing massage he eased her rigidity and hypnotically teased the responsive center until it peaked taut and appealing. Slowly his mouth enclosed the rosebud.

Again the guttural purr was repeated, Mitch reveling in her audible expression of ecstasy. His hand began to run down the shapely curve of her hip, then smoothed the flat plane of her abdomen as, simultaneously, his tongue erotically rotated about the tip of one breast, then trailed the fleshy divide between and repeated the intimate gesture with exacting sensitivity.

Del's tapered fingers ran through his raven hair, at first stroking the soft fullness in a contented fashion; but as Mitch's ardor increased, there came light tugs of euphoric response, and her body arched wantonly in natural accord. Languidly his mouth deserted her breast for the magnetism of a pair of moist, parted lips which provocatively enticed him to sample the unexplored recesses beyond. Hesitantly, then boldly, their tongues tested, then blended in feverish harmony, all the while Mitch's hand expertly gliding to the golden femininity below her undulating pelvis. With each excited breath and percussioned heartbeat, the concerto crescendoed, beginning pianissimo, then gradually escalating to forte.

Del's head thrashed wildly upon the pillow in what seemed a negative gesture, but Mitch did not relent, his free hand stroking her baby doll curls and flushed cheeks as he softly reassured her. "Easy, babe, easy . . . It's all right."

The melodic quality of his voice registering along with his worldly touch, she at last succumbed to his transcending orchestration. Repeatedly the thrill of a climactic finale waved over her damp body, and she clung fast to Mitch while experiencing the beautiful sensation of the unknown. Yet with the inevitable passing of the physical came the psychological, and like all receivers, she abdicated control to the giver.

Strong arms enfolded her, and with an easy, titillating roll she rested atop Mitch's muscular form. Methodically his arousing hands petted her back from the delicious depths of sensuality. The mood was lazy, the dying light muted as her shadowed eyes and grateful lips embraced their deliverer.

"I can feel, Mitch," came the husky murmur. "God! What have I missed?" A testimonial of joyful tears spilled onto his cheek as her mouth coveted his.

"You still have no conception, novice, but you're about to discover," he promised her, once more rotating her in his arms and sheathing her voluptuous body with his own.

His impassioned kiss expressed his gratitude as half-crazy with desire, his body became shifting and alive above hers. The conductive vibrations he created consumed them both, and before either realized, ardent passion engulfed them once more. Nothing, no one could stem the tide.

In natural response Del's thighs parted in invitation,

Mitch accepting in gentle entry. Again she tensed, her muscles constricting. But mindfully and carefully he seduced her to ease—his thrusts slow, sensual, deliriously hypnotic as he kissed the sensitive area behind her ear, the hollow of her throat, the high rise of her breasts.

She arched, moaned, then relaxed; he induced, held, then relented. Reverently his palms traced the length of her curved torso, halting at the feminine swell of her responsive hips. There they lingered, guiding, pacing, patiently awaiting until she followed the surging pressure and nothing else existed but the sway of bodies, the sounds of mutual need, and the sweltering, sweet heat of flamed union.

Slowly, heavenly, it evolved into an admission of loneliness, a proclamation of commitment—a man-woman bond as intensely radiant as a falling star's brilliance. It burst forth, a bright, celestial light, then slowly descended, disintegrated, until it was no more.

Spent, breathless, and fulfilled, they cloistered their shared emotion, snuggling nearer and communicating in tender touches. As her fingertips traced her deliverer's face, then smoothed the lips she would never forget, she spoke to him in a body language beyond words.

"You've renewed a disillusioned woman's belief in forgotten dreams—a cherished moment when Camelot's romance existed."

Receptively he pulled her closer against his attuned heart, his lips brushing her temple in silent persuasion.

"My love is real, Del. Believe in me," he seemed to say. "Believe in me!"

CHAPTER SEVEN

The days of the calendar passed, and with them came the fragile blossoming of love. In commemoration of Del's thirty-fifth birthday, Mitch presented her with two cherished gifts: a jade locket and an unforgettable night of tender intimacy. Thanksgiving followed, and again Del's blessings included Mitch's steadfast devotion. These wondrous days were exclusively theirs, the joy and solace that they discovered in their private lives coveted and completely separate from their public ones. The behind-closed-doors affair bothered Mitch incessantly, but realizing the instability of their budding relationship, he chose to give Del the time she obviously needed before pressing the point.

The Christmas season was upon them—peace on earth and goodwill toward men. And although the ideality of the theme was constantly being expounded, in actuality the humanitarianism was little practiced. The festive holidays took on an entirely different connotation for the officers of the Corpus Christi PD. It was the time when crimes against property and persons skyrocketed, suicides spiraled, and on-duty time escalated. As others sat cozy and safe in their comfortable niches, sharing eggnog and good cheer, the day and night watches kept vigil. Such was the case this particular night before Christmas Eve as Deeder and Del were returning to the station after a late supper break.

"Tell ya, Del," he was saying while scanning the streets in the hawkish way old beat cops do. "It's plumb discouragin' the way the rats come out of the woodwork around this time of year. It's almost enough to make an agnostic out of a believer."

She knew Deeder liked to cut loose with a shocking revelation every now and then just to rile her. Refusing to rise to the bait, she merely turned up the collar of her suede jacket and leaned the back of her head to the seat.

"You old reprobate!" she scoffed. "Don't try to lay that doomsday baloney on me. I'm on to your head games. Right about now you'd like me to go into my sociological theories so you can discredit them. Forget it! I'm not in the mood to debate." She cast him a sideways glance and caught the giveaway smirk tugging at the corner of his mouth.

"I was only making conversation, hot dog, but it appears you're a mite antagonistic tonight. Odd, seein' as how you been in such a dandy mood of late. Ya know, I was beginnin' to suspect ya might be courtin' yourself a fella—the way you've been kinda smilin' to yourself and sashayin' about. Guess it just goes to show ya that even I can make a slight miscalculation. Funny, though, I usually got a feel for these things." He tossed a devilish look in her direction, but she merely shrank deeper within her coat collar and continued to stare out upon the tinseled, glittered streets.

"Any unit clear and close. Assist the officer—domestic disturbance, three-oh-three Westport." The dispatch filled the sudden silence within the sedan.

"I ain't made a good hell raiser in a month of Sundays. Let's take it, Del!"

Before she could react, Deeder had the mike in hand, answering in an elated voice, "One-oh-five in the vicinity. Will respond."

"One-oh-five, clear," came the immediate go-ahead as Deeder made a sharp right and moved out.

"Yes, indeedy." He grinned. "Nothin' like a family ruckus to git the old adrenaline flowin'."

"Have you ever considered something simpler, like racquetball maybe?" Del gripped the armrest as he swerved around the next corner and screeched to a halt behind a patrol cruiser.

A swift jerk of a car door, followed by an instantaneous slam and three giant steps, produced Deeder on the front walk. "What you waitin' on, girl?" Impatiently he waved her on. "The action's inside!"

With a self-explanatory shove on the passenger door, Del refrained from voicing her opinion on his weird fetish for family squabbles as she trotted along in his wake.

As they made their approach, battle cries from within seeped through the ajar residence door. The weary age lines on Deeder's face virtually melted away as he crossed the threshold. "This one's gonna be a knock-down, drag-out for sure! Yup, gonna be real excitin'." Del's dark eyes rolled heavenward as she followed his husky frame inside.

"Sure glad to see you." A young patrolman, who looked one day fresh out of the academy, glanced solicitously in their direction. The rookie, too busy to be aware of how comical he appeared, held his open-arms stance and continued to pin a diminutive but raving woman in a corner.

"This thing's gotten way out of hand. We had it all under control and was escorting the husband out the door when, suddenly, all hell breaks loose." He dodged a kick to his shins, adding, "I got my hands full with a sidelines mother-in-law and three hysterical kids."

"Where's your partner, son?" Deeder glanced about the demolished room.

"That's just it." Again the rookie barely missed taking a shot from the dowdy woman's frumpy slippers. "The wife went berserk on us. She jumped Nixon, and they've been wrestling all over this place. I don't know where the old man went to. I think he's locked himself back up in the study."

Three distinct wails joined the mass confusion as the huddled children once more looked upon the stomped mess which had been their Christmas tree and presents. The shambled living quarters resembled Dodge City after a cattle stampede—tables overturned, bright wrappings and shattered ornaments strewn about, and, amid it all, a tumbled Christmas tree ridiculously twinkling red, blue, and yellow.

"Damn! They been doing that nonstop." The rookie groaned.

"Hang easy, son. Just keep baby-sittin' while we check on Nixon." Deeder motioned for Del to follow.

Only a short distance down the narrow hallway produced the distinct sounds of hand-to-hand combat—furniture toppling, exerted grunts, and filthy obscenities intensifying with each nearing step. At the doorway to a disheveled bedroom, both she and Deeder drew up simultaneously as their stupefied gazes drank in the ludicrous scene before them.

Nixon, a seasoned ten-year veteran, struggled to contain a giant of a woman who outweighed him by at least fifty pounds and stood a good head taller than he; and he wasn't faring very well. The Amazon had leeched herself onto his back and gripped handfuls of hair while trying to ride him to the floor. Through eyes that slitted from the strain on his scalp, Nixon caught the blur of Deeder's presence in the doorway. "Get her off!" he blurted before another vicious yank on his hair tossed his head back like a yo-yo.

"Thought you'd never ask." A wide grin broke Deeder's ruddy face as he ambled over, slipped a brawny arm beneath the woman's throat, and pried her backward until she released her grip.

Legs still wrapped about Nixon's waist and arms caught tightly in Deeder's grasp, the woman continued screaming curses while stretched like a rubber band between the two officers. Suddenly her legs released their scissors hold on Nixon's middle to begin kicking wildly and flogging his backside. Del could see Deeder's face turning red with strain as he tried to keep the enraged sow in check.

"Filthy pigs!" she screeched, wrenching and squirming in frenzied resistance.

"Get a hold of her legs!" Deeder panted above her yelps as Nixon dodged the strategically aimed kicks that threatened to incapacitate his love life.

"Don't suppose you wanna trade ends?" Nixon grunted breathlessly, clutching one ankle and dodging one-legged kicks while floundering to secure the other.

"Spare me the humor, Nixon, and let's git this beast to the car!" The earlier twinkle in Deeder's eyes diminished as the sweat upon his brow increased.

Engrossed in the bedlam before her, Del started at the feather-light tap on her shoulder. She turned to face a frail, little man with mousy eyes that matched his sallow complexion.

"Look, miss," he began, but then cringed as yet another bloodcurdling shriek came from the crazed Amazon. "I don't want no run-in with the law. It's just *her* I can't stand. All I meant to do was get my things and sneak out of here quietlike. But, oh, no! That's too civilized for her. We got to have a scene, and now look at the mess we're in!" His hollowed eyes searched Del's face for a shred of understanding.

"Just bide your time, and once this is resolved, I think you'll get your chance, Mr. . . . ah?"

"Curry," he said, his shoulders drawing even with his ears at his wife's renewed ranting.

"You bastards will pay hell taking me in!" Her body jerked convulsively as Nixon and Deeder snapped a pair of cuffs in place and began dragging her out the bedroom door. The meek spouse flattened against the wall at the fresh onslaught by his wife. "I'll get you for this, you little wimp! You just see if I don't."

Del stepped aside until the entourage had passed and then reassured the shaking wimp before catching up. "I suggest you be elsewhere when she's released. Tonight she'll be our guest, but tomorrow . . ." Her meaningful gaze conveyed her unspoken warning.

"Yes, ma'am." A faint smile registered his comprehension, and a few seconds later a soft "thanks," trailed her steps up the hall.

The children's wails and the mother-in-law's jeers joined the chaos as the procession moved through the living room and out the front door. Once on the front porch, the beast's struggles became maniacal, her threats and curses delivered with even greater intent. One after another, she made less than complimentary references to her captors' heritage and parentage while, in the process of the ensuing battle, her hiked housedress exposed indiscreet yards of flabby flesh.

The brisk night air soon became filled with her wild shrieks, but crazily, above it all, came the sweet, clear strands of "Silent night, holy night. All is calm, all is bright. . . ."

Disbelievingly Del's eyes darted to the candle-carrying carolers coming up the street. Their timing couldn't have been worse. For just as Deeder and Nixon were attempting to shove their 200-pound bundle into the police cruiser, the carolers drew directly alongside. Piously shocked, the ruffled reverend scooted his brood with "Move along, children . . . next house, please!" The absurdity mounted as Nixon slammed the back door on their raving captive, and then he and Deeder tried to hide her savage pummels upon the glass with their turned backs. With a paternal nod to the wide-eyed children, Deeder mumbled a superfluous "Nice evenin', ain't it?" as the crimson-faced reverend moved on by.

Del's usual calm reserve almost failed her, but she kept a tight rein on herself and resumed her position within the sedan. The sedan door eased open, and a curiously subdued Deeder slid to his place behind the wheel.

"Yes, indeedy!" She emulated his folksy twang. "Can't beat a family ruckus for getting the old adrenaline flowing!"

"Trouble with you, Del, is that you don't know when to shut up!" The engine turned over, the tires burned, and Del flipped on the car radio in lieu of Deeder's disgruntled company. Befittingly a local DJ signed off his program with an ironic "Merry Christmas to all; and to all a good night!" *Appropriate,* Del thought, the slow smile forming on her lips breaking into a full-fledged grin.

With a surrendering sigh Mitch pulled Del closer against his primed body, his fingertip cupping her chin and lifting her confused eyes to his. "Why do I have the distinct feeling that I'm making love to only part of a woman? Though your body's going through the motions, your mind isn't on us. Where are you, Del?"

Regretful guilt washed over her as she rolled atop him and began to run her fingers through his tousled hair. "I'm sorry. Is it that obvious?"

His affirmative nod carried an amused smile. "You're still dwelling on those kids, aren't you?"

She laid her head upon his furry chest, her hand lazily tracing the dark hairline that trailed down his taut abdomen. The exciting tingle her very touch ignited spurred Mitch's desire once more.

"As much as I'd love to take advantage of that sexy body of yours and ignore the obvious lack of enthusiasm, I'm conceited enough to believe I deserve more. So"—he playfully slapped her fanny—"for purely selfish reasons I'm going to absolve your guilty conscience and rectify the injustice of a presentless Christmas for the Curry children."

With a flip of the covers his lithe figure sprang from the bed. "Upsy-daisy, woman. We've got a big morning ahead playing Santa Claus."

Jerking upright, the sheet discreetly draped over her breasts, Del studied him curiously. Though a light smile touched his lips, a resoluteness tinted his eyes clear blue. "You're serious, aren't you?" she asked, astonishment animating her voice.

"Of course. We can't have three little kids going through Christmas without a visit from Santa Claus any more than we can deprive ourselves of a lovemaking Christmas Eve."

Drawing to her knees, Del reached out a hand and pulled Mitch back atop the bed with her. Instantly her mouth mazed his laughing face with short, grateful kisses. "I don't know whether you're a devil or an angel," she said teasingly, her face snuggling against his morning-shadowed cheek.

"Both, my love. You mustn't ever forget that! But now . . ." He pulled her with him off the bed, his arms enclosing her tempting body and pulling her near. "But now . . ." For an aching moment his hungry eyes drank in the seductiveness of her naked form, but then, tweaking her aloof nose, he forced himself to tend to the business at hand. "We have work to do, Miss Harris." Reluctantly he released his hold upon her soft flesh and moved toward the adjoining bathroom. A gush of shower water echoed above his shouted orders of the day.

"First, you check and be sure that the beast is still a guest of the city jail. Next, we go to the biggest, most elaborate toy store we can find and select our gifts. Then onward and forward to the Currys' with some cock-and-bull story about how Santa made a delivery mistake. And last, but surely not least . . ." His dark head peeked around the corner, and he shot her a suggestive wink.

With a hurl of a pillow from the bed, Del feigned indignation, laughing. "You're impossible, Mitchell Parrish—an out-and-out opportunist!"

"And you love it," he retaliated, ducking and grinning before retreating.

Hours later, snuggled among pillows beneath a cozy afghan, they lay in each other's arms upon the plush carpet, not speaking, but merely enjoying the sentimentality about them—the merry dance of twinkling bulbs upon the old-fashioned Christmas tree, the singular fragrance of evergreen, the sweet bouquet of wine upon smooth lips, and the camaraderie of warm flesh against flesh.

As Del lay with her head propped upon Mitch's shoulder, a particular ornament upon the Scotch pine caught her eye: cherub-faced angels twirling at the end of a red velvet ribbon. The outline became hazy as she reflected upon the previous delight of three semiangelic but very needy children.

From the moment they'd approached the Currys' front door, bundles of gaily wrapped packages in hand, Mitch had been in total control. On the doorstep she'd voiced her misgivings that the children would remember yesterday's fiasco and hate her for her part in it. Mitch merely grinned.

"How can any child refuse a woman bearing gifts?" he'd said cajolingly. "Besides, you're not the Wicked Witch of the East."

There'd been only time for a quick miffed glance before the door swung open to reveal a green-eyed freckled face little miss standing knob-high. From then on it was Mitch's charisma all the way. In seconds he'd charmed the six-year-old toothless wonder into believing that Santa had made a delivery mistake and that it was perfectly all right for them to be asked inside. Equally as impressive was the fact that within minutes her two brothers were coerced into joining the make-believe, the middle child most willingly, the older, reluctantly.

"Surprised they're bringin' somethin' in, 'steada draggin' somethin' out," Nicky, the twelve-year-old ramrod of the clan, had said. Though he'd seen Del only briefly, he hadn't forgotten the circumstances. His insolent look knifed through her, but quickly Mitch took charge.

"Look, son, we don't intend to impose, only drop off a few presents." With a level gaze and commanding tone Mitch tempered the boy's initial hostility.

As the other two children tore into their presents with whoops of glee, Nicky had stood apart and aloof. Slightly unnerved by his remoteness, Del found herself repeatedly glancing to him from amid the pandemonium of the merrymakers. Intuitively she knew that beneath the manly veneer lurked a vulnerable boy who longed for the normality which other children took for granted. She knew . . . but how to penetrate that hard shell was entirely another matter.

With Sarah, the adorable youngest, and Jeff, the easygoing middle child, completely immersed in their unexpected bounty, there remained only Nicky, the hard-core non-believer, to win over. Del knew his exoneration would not come easily.

"Nicky?" Her hands had shaken as she held out her offering. The moment was to become one of the most poignant in her life. Many times she would recall that crucial instant when Nicky's decision-weighted eyes met hers.

Then Mitch's arm had dropped about the boy's slim shoulders, and ten weighty words swung the balance in her favor: "It's Christmas, son. No charity, just a token of friendship." He'd nudged Nicky toward her.

In one swift but immensely significant move, Nicky had forgiven, hugging her neck in a rough but intense clutch as she whispered, "Merry Christmas, Nicky," and then handed him the present. If she lived to be a hundred, Del would never forget the emotion of the moment. No more than she could erase the memory of the mood that prevailed when Mitch and she sat absorbed in the infectious joy of the children. Regret wound around their hearts, emphasizing the empty chambers of their lives and binding them in yet one other invisible way.

"You're a good man, Mitchell Parrish," she'd whispered adoringly.

"Do good men, like good boys, receive their wish for Christmas, too?" he'd asked.

"If it's within reason." Del remembered holding her breath along with his gaze.

"At this moment what I want, more than anything else in the world, is for us to go home and love the night away."

An involuntary blink of an eye drew the cherub-faced angels dangling from the ribbon into clear view once more. Del stirred against Mitch's shoulder with an expressive sigh. The enriching experience of the day's events conjured depressing memories of estranged Christmas Eves when there had been no one to care and no one with whom to share. The lonely ache of a thousand loveless days and nights pierced her mind and heart. Before Mitch, had her life been so empty? Could she allow it to be again? The possibility was unthinkable. Compulsively she turned to him with an enraptured smile.

"I doubt our celebration would be considered traditional," she murmured, kissing Mitch's muscular shoulder and then gliding her silky hair across his chest as she resituated her head in his lap.

"When have we ever been conventional?" His hand slid within her wayward curls, fondling the soft strands suggestively.

Seductively her lips traced kisses over his firm abdomen. She loved the texture of his skin, the maverick scent combined with the manly blend of bronze flesh and dark hair. Her tapered nails ran a wanton path along his upper torso. The moves were slow, spellbinding, as if she were memorizing every lithe inch of him by blind feel.

Leisurely and deliberately her kisses moved upward, her soft mouth teasing along his pulsing neck and ending at the base of his ear. "If I have my way, this night will be not only unconventional, Counselor, but unforgettable." Her dark eyes lit with premeditated intent as she purposely lifted her wineglass and trickled a trail of nectar down his chest. "From now on, wherever you are and whoever you're with on Christmas Eve, you'll recall this moment and remember me," she promised him in a husky voice a second before her tongue followed the meandering droplets of red wine. Sweeping over erect nipples, across a quivering diaphragm, her tantalizing touch moved lower still, until a shudder of passion tightened the length of Mitch's body and an agonized groan escaped him.

The urgent force of his arms crushing her to him took

her breath away. "God! Gypsy nymph! What kind of madness are you weaving?"

His breath grew short and labored, and she could feel the effects of her seduction hard and throbbing against her flushed skin. Provocatively her shadowed lashes lifted, unveiling dark orbs of desire which cast their black magic all about them. Her persuasive fingertips smoothed his raven hair, and then, demandingly, she pulled his lips against her parted mouth. The heady taste of wine upon her tongue titillated Mitch's senses. A flame kindled deep within him welling up and setting his flesh afire.

"I love you, gypsy," she heard him whisper through the vacuum that swirled and swept them beyond boundary or dimension. Deliriously her palms massaged his damp back, then glided across his tensed abdomen and caressed his most sensitive region. The exacting pressure was precisioned; the stroked timing, experienced perfection. His eyes closed with a deep, savoring sigh as he gave himself up to the protégée who had now become the master. The pressure relented, and then the guiding weight of her palms upon his shoulders pressed him flat upon his back. Again her mouth and hands explored his body. Only this time the intensity of the contact ignited their passions to a fevered pitch.

"It's so easy to make love to you, Mitch." The sultry quality of her voice stirred him as much as her smooth, salacious touch. Through glazed eyes he took in the shimmer of her exceptional body as she slowly eased herself upon him and began to move in expert rhythm.

His hands cupped her firm breasts. Beneath them he could feel the centers tense as her rhythm increased. He couldn't stand the sensual tension any longer. She was driving him crazy! With one smooth roll he assumed the dominant position and increased the tempo while tasting of passion's extract upon and beyond her desirous lips.

Ecstasy awaited them only thrust and rises away. Her arms wrapped about his neck possessively as her breath grew warm and rapid against his cheek. His pace heightened, her body arched, and simultaneously they moaned in a blend of wild kisses and mutual release.

Through the haze of unequaled repletion Mitch felt the gentleness of her hand against his cheek, heard the sincerity of the words which would become indelible in his mind. "I love you, darling. Merry Christmas." She had fulfilled her promise. There would never be another Christmas Eve that didn't carry the memory of Del.

CHAPTER EIGHT

Del stretched lazily, savoring the easy respite of a day off. Her hand reached to the pillow beside her and touched the indented impression where Mitch's head had lain.

"New Year's Eve," she murmured contentedly. Not only was she dwelling in the clover of actually having a holiday, but she was reveling in the wondrous addition of Mitch into her life. The outgoing year had brought her joy beyond words. Unexpectedly she'd received a reprieve from her solitary existence from a strong man whose patience and compassion had freed her to love again. Their arrangement was so comfortable. For they were well suited as lovers and companions, and thus far their ideological differences had been avoided by unspoken mutual agreement.

Del gave a pampered wriggle beneath the downy comforter. After all, she had the best of two worlds: Mitch in the privacy of the bedroom minus the censure of her peers that came with public acknowledgment. She knew it wasn't a realistic arrangement and was cowardly on her part, but it was so divine to have everything going her way for once. Obstinately she tried to disregard the pangs of conscience that kept hovering in the shadows of her mind. But try as she might, Del knew that Mitch's compliance with her ground rules was a grudging concession on his part.

She knew he wasn't totally happy with their situation. He wanted more. Though he hadn't voiced it, she sensed his resentment of her opposing views. He expected an open commitment to be made. But she wasn't ready, and didn't know when she would be. It all was moving too fast for a woman who had spent so many years in reclusion. The option to remain there was not only secure but compelling.

Thoughts of the future plagued Del. Though it was New Year's Eve, the time of new beginnings, she still preferred the security of the old. With an unconscious sigh she rolled from beneath the covers. She wished she could hold back the hands of time, preserve the easy flow of her and Mitch's involvement. Before midnight she would learn that the wish wasn't any more possible than altering fate.

The day progressed uneventfully. Del lolled away her time by taking down the Christmas decorations and storing them away in the attic for another year. It was busywork to help her get through the hours without Mitch. For whenever he wasn't with her, he was constantly on her mind. Unwillingly she'd find herself reminiscing about the ring of his laughter, the constant mood changes of his eyes, or the memory of his touch. Boldly and heedlessly she'd fallen head over heels in love with Mitchell Parrish. She hadn't meant to, hadn't realized she had until it was too late. From that very first electrifying contact between them, months ago during a late-night chance meeting in her office, he'd marked her as his woman. She had fought it, even denied it, but the love affair had developed as naturally and inevitably as life itself.

Again she found herself wondering how fate had selected them as partners, two entirely different individuals with such opposing views. The chemistry between them was explosive, and the end results could be disastrous for them both. But just one look, one touch, one kiss, and they'd become helplessly ensnared in an emotional web from which there was no escape. Against all the odds and in spite of themselves, they'd fallen in love. And where in the hell would it lead?

The chime of her door saved Del from the disturbing possibilities. With a quick check of herself in the hall mirror she flounced her curls and went to the door.

"Delivery for a Miss Harris." An impeccably dressed messenger held out a large, flat box tied in green ribbon. "Sign here, please." A clipboard was thrust beneath her nose. Scribbling her signature, Del gazed dumbfoundedly back at the man as he gave her a standard "Thank you, and Happy New Year."

Softly shutting the door, Del tucked the box under her arm and strolled back toward the couch. Animation lit her eyes as they wandered over the distinctive emblem of Saks Fifth Avenue scrolled across the linen lid. That store is in Houston. Not exactly an across-town delivery, she mused, but only briefly as she became cognizant of Mitch's distinct style. Only he did things in such a grand manner. Feeling especially fortunate and pampered, she nearly burst with anticipation before her fumbling fingers could undo the wrappings.

Immediately her hands recognized the luxuriance of satin beneath them. Raising the garment from the box, she admired the full-length beige slip a second before her eyes were drawn again to the box and yet another present within.

Slowly, disbelievingly, she unfolded a delicately hand-crocheted dress from its cardboard lair. Tan and intricately woven, with side slits cut mid-thigh, cuffed sweater sleeves, and a daring V neckline trimmed in brown velvet, the designer dress fell gracefully to the floor. It had to have been conceived with her in mind; from the femininity of the material to the provocativeness of the style, it complimented her.

Frivolously she indulged herself, holding the dress in front of her and waltzing to the mirror. The extravagance of the gown, coupled with the excited glow of her nutmeg eyes, produced an intriguing look. Del stared at the image, wondering if she shared anything in common with the lovely creature in the mirror. The gift, like Mitch, brought out dormant qualities from deep within her. Also, like Mitch, the gift was unusual, unexpected, and carried a hint of obligation. Reluctantly she lowered the dress, turning away from the mirrored fantasy and back to the present.

Returning to the torn wrappings, she spread the gown over the back of the couch and began to search the box for a card. It was there, as she had known it would be. Hesitantly her shaky hands unfolded the note.

"It reminded me of how lovely you are and I couldn't resist. Have made reservations at Christy's on the Bay for eight. Tonight I intend to show this town how very fortunate I am! Love, Mitch."

The card slipped from her trembling fingers as her gaze riveted on the obligating gown. *No! She simply wasn't ready to risk exposure.* Not that she thought any of her acquaintances would patronize the elite Christy's, but knowing the notoriety that surrounded Mitchell's public life, she feared disclosure by eager gossips and press. As yet she wasn't mentally prepared to give up their fairy-tale romance and face the realities of their lives. It was insensitive of Mitch to expect it.

Her hands lighted upon the cool satin, rubbing the lustrous material thoughtfully. But what if she rejected his offer and didn't accompany him tonight? Wouldn't she lose by default? Her tormented mind vacillated between dissenting factions. It wasn't fair of Mitch to manipulate her capitulation, but it was so very like him. His week-old words came back to haunt her. "Which are you? A devil or an angel?" she had asked. "Both, my love, you mustn't ever forget that!" he'd warned.

"Damn it, Mitch! Not now! I can't handle it!" She moaned, her fist pounding the cushions frustratingly. "I need time," she argued aloud. *No! What you need, girl, is a drink and some calm, logical strategy,* she reasoned. After rising to her feet and retreating to behind the bar, she splashed an ample amount of Scotch into a glass, diluted it with water, and then began to pace the den like a caged animal. *You'll dissuade him from a night on the town,* she plotted. *You'll explain how you'd envisioned a cozy New Year's Eve for just the two of you and convince him how very special it could be!*

She stopped in mid-stride, took an encouraging gulp, and then shuddered with its burn. She hated Scotch, but it seemed apropos: retribution for her sins. How could she be so calloused? So conniving? She'd never used feminine wiles before, let alone contemplated using her body as bait to stall Mitch's dreams of commitment. But if she allowed him prematurely to subject her to the criticism that she most certainly would come under, wouldn't that be more damaging than the façade of secrecy she insisted upon?

She drank down the last of the Scotch, and then slammed the empty glass to the bar. She didn't know who was right or wrong anymore. All she knew for certain was that she just wasn't able to cope with outside censure right now. Selfish and immature as it was, she couldn't give up the make-believe world that she'd locked Mitch and herself away in. She needed it just a little longer. Maybe a month or two down the line, she could face whatever the cynics threw at her, but not now, damn it! Not now!

With a final brake, Mitch's Cadillac Seville rolled to a stop in front of Del's home. He turned off the engine, looked at the bouquet of roses resting beside him, and then sagged back against the seat. Bribes! All his carefully contrived plans had been nothing more than bribes to smooth his way out of seclusion.

He didn't know why he had selected New Year's Eve as the time to make his move. Maybe it had something to do with resolution. For he most certainly wanted to resolve the grating feelings that had gnawed away at him lately: feelings like being a kept lover, good enough to warm his woman's bed, but far too notorious for the lady to admit in public. He knew the stigma that surrounded them was more complicated than that. Yet a certain amount of truth lay within the allegation.

Why couldn't things be simpler for them? Hadn't they had to overcome enough obstacles in order to realize their love? And regardless of how he'd tried to convince himself otherwise, *it was love!* Only once before in his life had he cared for a woman in the way he did for Del, and then he'd been foolish enough to step aside for a career. *He'd be damned if he'd do it again!* After all, it wasn't as if he were asking her to give it up; only to modify it so that their personal life wouldn't be so detrimentally affected.

Mitch flexed his tense shoulder muscles and absently reached out to touch a soft rose petal. The velvety texture reminded him of Del's creamy skin. He was becoming obsessed with her. So much so that he couldn't stand the thought of being unable to include her fully in his life. And, he guessed if he were honest with himself, he resented not being invited to share her wholly. Why should their amnesty be only in the bedroom? Surely a workable truce could be reached professionally. The bigoted animosity that her co-workers felt for him was as unreasonable as Del's ambiguous fear of it. Oh, she'd never mentioned her fellow officers' opinion of him. In fact, she hadn't given any reason for their seclusion other than her preference for privacy. But their dislike of him was there all right! Just beneath the surface and out of reach!

Determinedly Mitch reached for the final bribe, swung open the car door, and then stood for a long, contemplating moment, staring up at Del's front door. *Damn them all! The time to remove the last obstacle was now. He'd been patient long enough!* With a final slam of the door Mitch nervously adjusted his tie, then assumed one of his most winning smiles and strode purposely toward the town house.

"You're early." The door swung open before he had a chance to knock. He hoped that she hadn't observed him sitting like a twit out front for the past five minutes. Passing her the roses, he tried to act nonchalant.

"I must be. You're not dressed yet." His eyes roamed the gold silk wrapper which clung to her delectable curves like a thin film of honey.

"They're lovely, Mitch. Thank you." After a light kiss on his cheek she retreated to the kitchen and began to arrange the flowers in a vase. Having thrown his topcoat over a chair, he followed to stand at the edge of the counter, ignoring the anxious bands tightening about his chest.

"I thought we'd have a drink." She answered his unspoken question as if reading his mind. The tense lines about his eyes softened slightly. "What would you like?" Her smile bordered on wicked as her dark eyes lit upon the manly bulge straining against his tight-fitting pants. No matter what the circumstances, just the mere sight of Del in something revealing incited a spontaneous response from him.

"Besides the obvious, Scotch straight up if you have it." His returning smile sent a suggestive thrill up Del's spine.

"I think I can handle that." She sashayed past him, the

smell of her perfume lingering in her wake. The omens were good, she thought. Maybe her scheming had all been for nothing. Mitch's desire for her might relieve her in more ways than one. She mixed the drinks, trying to overcome the guilt she felt for deliberately undermining his plans for the evening.

"Here you go, Counselor." She handed him an especially tall drink and curled up beside him on the couch. Randomly her gaze roved over his smartly dressed person, taking in the brown silk suit, two-toned cocoa shirt and white collar, tiger's-eye cuff links, and kid-leather loafers. "You're looking exceptionally handsome tonight." Her hand touched his perfectly French-knotted tie.

His warm one closed over hers, bringing the fingertips to his lips and gently kissing each one. "When a man's stepping out with a beautiful woman, he should play the part to the hilt." He noted the ever-so-slight stiffening of her fingertips beneath his lips. "You did receive my gift and note today, didn't you?" He calmly studied her reaction.

"Yes. As usual, they both were exquisite, Counselor." She feigned a smile, withdrew her hand, and then sipped her drink. "I was surprised, though. I had thought that we'd celebrate New Year's Eve . . . a little less conventionally."

The memory of their Christmas celebration still fresh in Mitch's mind, her subtle implication became quite clear. "Well, sweetheart, I must admit the offer's tempting. . . ." His knuckles traced the plunging neckline of her robe contemplatingly before his fingers closed about the lapels and he drew her against his mouth. As he released her ripe lips, his eyes grew that steadfast gray she'd learned to respect as he murmured, "But I think we should begin our new year in a slightly more traditional way."

Del's heart raced within her breast. She was up against

the king of wily persuasion, and her coquettish tactics had been nipped in the bud. Though the real conflict had been cleverly masked in the façade of a frivolous night on the town, both she and Mitch realized the greater controversy, where each stood on it, and the detrimental consequences of those prideful stands.

"I hate to rush you, but our reservation is for eight." Mitch, direct as usual, forced the delicate issue. She had no way of knowing that behind the calm smile and unyielding eyes lay a tormented man who ached for a positive response.

"Humor me this one night, Mitch. Please let's stay home." Her toffee eyes were never more beautiful, the grazing touch of the back of her hand upon his cheek never more communicative, and the excited rise and fall of cleavage peeking at the divide of her robe never more enticing. He was a man torn apart by principle and desire.

His hand stopped her appealing touch with one thorough press. Clasping it tightly to thwart her pulling away, he softly, but adamantly, ended the pretext of superfluous banter. "I've *been* humoring you, Del. This privacy trip has about run its course. I want this night out as much as I want you, and I don't think I have to explain how strong that need is. Our past experiences speak for themselves." All signs of subterfuge left his voice.

"Please, Mitch, don't force this. I need time . . . just a little longer. . . ." The plea drifted as she glanced up into his unrelenting features, her body freezing upon contact with the frigidity in his eyes.

"Time! Time for what, Del? Do you think a few more days, weeks, or months will erase an animosity that has slowly risen with my reputation? Resentment isn't something that mends itself with time. It festers and grows like a malignant cancer. Evading it doesn't make it go away. It only complicates everything." Reading her reclusive tendencies as she shrank farther from him, Mitch grabbed her shoulders impulsively.

"Don't shy away from reality and me, Del. What am I supposed to do? Just wait in the wings until you decide you can face the heat? Will the cracks from your narrow-minded, cliquish comrades disturb you that much?"

"That's unfair, Mitch, and you know it!" She shook off his grip and jumped to her feet. The tie of her robe had loosened in the interim. As if in symbolic rejection, she yanked it tighter about her sleek form. "Why are you insisting on this now? Everything's been so good . . . so right. Is it absolutely crucial that we declare ourselves at this very moment? Come spring I'll take the lieutenant's exam, and at least the criticism of us will be tempered. Rank and file do not openly harass their superiors."

"God!" He sprang to his feet, his hand running through his hair frustratingly. "I don't believe we're having this ridiculous conversation. Come spring! Do you honestly believe we can keep our association a secret until then? And tell me what in the name of God would we accomplish by that besides stilling the acid tongues that will be just as derogatory in the spring? I love you, Del." He turned and faced her, the searing intensity within his gaze melting her resistance. "And you love me. That's true now. But do you really think it can survive the kind of isolation you want to subject us to?"

"Yes!" Her chin rose, her body stiffened, and her tone grew strong with conviction. "You have to understand my predicament. I've struggled hard to get where I am, to earn the recognition I've gained so far. All I'm asking for is a little time—time enough to gain an exempt position. What logical reason do you have to object?"

"Pride, that's the reason, love, and if you don't understand a man's pride, you mock him. I'm not a leper to be exiled to a Posturepedic mattress and goose-down pillows. I'm a vital man who includes the world about him . . . good, bad, or indifferent." In two long strides he crossed the space between them and yanked her possessively into his arms. Her heart beat wildly against his chest. "I can't live my life in a closet, Del. I need and want you in every part of it. I never could settle for a segment of anything." His large hands ran within her curls, clutching the strands in unspoken desperation.

"I can't abide the thought of your being ashamed of me. Instead, I need my woman to stand against the world with me." His voice broke under the strain. Del's forehead pressed to his shoulder, rocking back and forth miserably. Sick with conflict, she leaned closer against him for support. Her breasts felt soft and yielding upon him, and Mitch fought down the irrational impulse to lower her to the carpet and love her to submission.

"I'm not ashamed of you, Mitch. You're distorting everything. You know that I love you, and you say that you love me. Yet you place me in the impossible position of making a choice that is nonexistent."

His fingertip cupped her quivering chin, forcing her misty eyes to his imploring ones. "You still don't understand, do you? The choice is very real, Del. You can't have it both ways: me and obscurity. It's a package deal: notoriety and the controversial counselor. I'm either the man you love or the one you loved *once.* Which is it, Del?"

A tremor of pure fear passed through her body. One look into his uncompromising eyes told her she had to commit herself or chance losing him forever. The clock on the mantel chimed eight. It was too late to keep the reservation. God help her! It was probably too late for everything! "Oh, please, Mitch, don't do this to us. Wait—"

"I have waited," he interrupted, despair cracking his voice. Tenderly he pinned her stricken face between his hands, his defeated eyes making love to her a final time. At last he uttered the words that spoke of a past tense. "I did it *for* us, Del, not *to* us." His familiar hands lifted, and he walked for his coat.

Del couldn't believe what was happening. It was like a nightmare from which she couldn't arouse herself. "Don't you walk out of my life, Mitchell Parrish," she warned. "Don't you dare—"

The door slammed, leaving only the methodic tick of the clock as Del crumpled to her knees beside the coffee table, buried her head in her arms, and sobbed over the lost hours they would never share.

Overwhelmed with grief, she alternately cried, cursed, and then subsided into a dazed reflection of the love affair that had cost her all—the lover who had demanded a price too dear to pay, and the depleting heartbreak from which she might never recover. Why, damn it, why, had she been foolish enough to subject herself to love again? Didn't it always turn on her? Abuse her?

The clock chimed midnight. Swollen and numb, Del struggled to her feet and clicked on the radio in an attempt to blot out the anguishing emptiness that surrounded her. A broadcast from a downtown hotel filled the room with its taunting merriment.

"Should auld acquaintance be forgot/And never brought to mind . . . /Should auld acquaintance be forgot/ And days of auld lang syne."

The miserable ache returned with greater ferocity. She'd live through this night in spite of herself, she promised. *But would she ever live down the memory of the man who had caused it?*

CHAPTER NINE

Mitch lay amid the crumpled covers. With trepidation he massaged his aching eyes. This ungodly morning hangover rounded out a miserable series of seven—seven consecutive twenty-four-hour periods of nightly stupors and morning convalescence. Yet the Chivas wasn't working its magic. Oh, he'd been successful in his attempt to obliterate Del's memory while anesthetizing himself with quality Scotch, but always there came the morning after, the conscious thoughts of Del, and the return of the pains in his head and his heart. Unshaved and uncaring, he rolled onto his side and let his hand rest on the receiver of the phone. How many times in the past seven days had he repeated the procedure? First cursing her and his hangover and then reminiscing about all that had been good between them while impulsively reaching for the phone.

God only knew how much he wanted to pick up that receiver, dial her familiar number, and hear that sultry "hello" that had always facinated him so. Even when he was under the twilight effects of the liquor, the vivid recollections of her haunted him. He never imagined he could miss someone so much!

His fingers tightened on the receiver. It would take such little effort to lift it off its cradle—such little effort, but so much pride. What would he say? That he'd been wrong? Ask that they put the episode behind them and go on? As if it didn't matter! As if it were possible! And he wasn't totally wrong—maybe not a hundred percent right, but certainly not completely wrong! His head throbbed as his fingers eased their grip.

He was going to have to cope a little longer. Surely if he did, one of two things would happen: Either she'd realize that she loved and needed him as much as he did her, or eventually the passing of time would heal his wounds and Del Harris would become a memory he could live with. So what if she was beautiful of face, mind, and body? In his life there had been a lot of beautiful women. Maybe not as exceptional as Del was in so many ways, but wasn't life merely an unending cycle of compromises? This was just one more he'd have to accept.

The phone shrilled beside him, tensing every nerve in his body. Could it be Del? Would fate be so kind? He jerked the receiver to his ear with an anxious "hello."

"*Michel?*"The voice on the other end faltered. Only one person ever pronounced his name with that foreign accent —Ramona Valez—Ramona, once the center of his world and now the prima donna contralto for the New York Met.

"Yes, Ramona," he replied wearily.

"Did I awaken you, *mi amor*?" Her alto accent reminded him of sultry Acapulco nights and soft Spanish guitars.

"No. I'm always up by the crack of ten. To what do I owe this unexpected honor?" he asked, barely managing to disguise the disappointment in his voice.

"I've called to thank you for your last favor and impose upon you for yet another."

"I'm almost afraid to ask what it is. Your last request, that I defend your cousin Dolphus on that cocaine charge, stirred considerable criticism of my ethics. Ugly rumors have been circulating about my suspected affiliation with the *familia.*"

"I am truly sorry, Michel, if I have caused for you an embarrassment."

"You know me well enough to realize that I'm seldom embarrassed. Besides, I was well compensated for any inconvenience. If nothing else, my fee should tell you that I never mix favors with business." A faint smile stole across his lips.

"*Por nada.* I can well afford your favors." He could fairly imagine the slightly askew grin on her pouty lips.

"And what would you have me do now, Ramona? But I warn you, if another of your distant relatives needs legal counsel, the most I can offer is an excellent referral."

"Nothing quite so serious, *mi amor.* I am in town to attend the fund-raising dinner for the new music hall tonight. You have heard of this affair?

"Mmmm." Mitch closed his eyes and rubbed his temple. "And you need an escort," he astutely guessed.

"Would you be so kind, Michel? It would be nice to see each other again, if only for old times' sake."

There had been a time in his life when he would have responded without hesitation to the ebony-eyed beauty, a time when her wish had been his command. But now she was only a friend in need, and he an acquaintance who didn't have the heart or will to refuse.

"Sure," he responded less than enthusiastically. "When and where should I pick you up?"

"My day is very full. Shall we say about sevenish . . . the cocktail lounge of the La Quinta Hotel?"

"I'll be there," he confirmed.

"*Gracias, mi amor.* I look forward to being with you again."

"It ought to be a grand reunion. *Hasta luego,*" he said.

"Yes, till later, Michel." She laughed at his Spanish accent and then hung up.

Mitch replaced the receiver and lay thinking about Ramona for a moment. Within her veins flowed two intriguing bloods: the blue of Spanish aristocracy and the red wild of the Apache. From her mother she had inherited her classic good looks and fine manners; from her father, her fierce pride and passion for life. But her voice was another thing all together. Pure, rich, and moving, it was a heaven-sent gift which had gained for her worldwide acclaim but cost her the man she'd left behind. A young and struggling lawyer couldn't compete with the fanatical ambition which fed her quest for fame. She had declined Mitch's marriage proposal, choosing instead to devote herself to a career that offered even greater adulation. It had been merely a necessary compromise on her part, yet absolutely devastating to him.

A melancholy smile touched his lips as he ran a hand through his mussed hair and sat up on the edge of the bed. His bloodshot eyes rested on the damned phone once more. Yes, he thought bitterly, life most definitely was a never-ending cycle of concessions. With supreme effort he forced himself to his feet and then trudged toward the revitalizing shower.

The Waterin' Hole clamored with the typical sounds of a bar—wailing country tunes on the jukebox, the whoosh and thud of shuffleboard mingling with the sharp crack of billiard balls, the tink of beer bottles, and the boisterous frivolity of the patrons. The smell of popcorn merged with the blue haze of smoke hovering in the dimly lit room as Deeder and Del entered. Normally Del didn't patronize the cop hangout, but tonight she just couldn't face going home and waiting for the phone call that never came. Tonight Deeder's suggestion that they stop off for a cold one appealed to her. Why not? It wasn't as if anyone were waiting on her. Only Mama Cat cared if she existed at all, and only then because she provided the basic necessities for her. It wasn't very consoling to know that a dumb, spoiled animal was all that missed you!

"Looks like there's a couple of empty stools down at the end of the bar by Ski and Horton. Let's git to 'em before someone else grabs 'em." Deeder nudged her back, and they moved down the room-length bar to random shouts of "Hey, Deed! Word's out . . . physicals next week . . . better drink that light beer!" and "Your old lady called twice. She said to tell ya it's bingo night and for you to eat out. Better watch him, Del. Whenever he drinks whiskey, he goes crazy like an Indian!"

Del ignored the friendly taunts, continuing to work her way to the empty stools beside Ski and Horton and then easing herself onto one.

"Two drafts, Mickey." Deeder took up a position beside her, an uncommon scowl etched upon his normally pleasant face.

"I didn't think the temperance leaguer would be caught dead in this den of iniquity." Horton greeted them, his perpetually rascal features lighting up as he slid a bowl of popcorn past Del and down to Deeder.

"Maybe it ain't the booze, but the company that annoys her!" Deeder shot back, then hoisted his beer and downed half the brew in two long gulps.

Del shrugged her shoulders at Horton and then sipped from the frosted mug before her.

Always the agitator, Horton winked at his consort in mischief, Steneski, and then leaned across Del to needle Deeder a little more. "Say, Deed, just before you came in, the guys and I were theorizing on who the phantom cartoonist could be. Popular opinion tags you as the sketch addict. Come on, 'fess up! Hell, we ain't gonna snitch you off. We might even give you a medal!"

Del looked from Deeder's noncommittal face into Horton's expectant one. Everyone had a Horton type in his past—an instigator synonymous with devilish pranks and riding people high. Usually the remembrance was linked with alma maters and crazy times. Steneski could also be stereotyped—the quiet sidekick who followed suit without question and reveled in the leftover limelight of his comedian counterpart. But Del found herself completely in the dark about what they were up to this time.

"The phantom cartoonist? What kind of malarkey are you making up now, Horton?" She quizzed him, knowing full well that he was probably suckering her in, but unable to ignore the curiosity getting the best of her.

"You mean to tell me that you haven't heard of the phantom? Where've you been for the past few weeks?" Horton truly looked astonished. "Well," he continued, "it seems that unflattering caricatures of Captain Stonewall Higgins have been mysteriously appearing on the bulletin board outside the squad room. Usually they're slamming Stonewall's latest crusade, cleverly depicting him as the nerd that he is, and always scrawled in the lower right-hand corner are the words 'The Phantom.' "You remember Stonewall's most recent vendetta—our raids against the X-rated Bayou Drive-Inn?

Del gave a short nod, twisting the frosted mug before her impatiently.

"Well, the phantom's retaliatory cartoon sketched Stonewall as slinking into his office with the confiscated triple X reels tucked under his arm, a crafty grin slitting his bulldog jowls, and was captioned 'The Phantom's Hypocrisy of the Week Award—presented to Stonewall Higgins for his unselfish dedication to private censorship and porno.' "

Del broke into a wide grin. Captain Stonewall Higgins was a pain in everyone's side—one of those obnoxious supervisors who suffered from the "BIG I, little you" syndrome; as Deeder so aptly put it, "he swats flies with a sledgehammer."

"It's becoming a game of strategy," Horton explained. "I'm sure you recall how Stonewall used to sneak around the corner like some five-year-old playing I Spy in order to catch one of us conducting personal business during on-duty time? Well, now he's been hiding behind the squad room door, hoping to catch the phantom when next he strikes." Horton looked over at the unconcerned Deeder, who sat staring straight ahead. "But our phantom's shrewd. He lets Higgins wait it out for days at a stretch and never shows up. Then, just when our illustrious captain thinks the fun and games are over and settles back into his routine, zappo! the phantom strikes again! I love it!" he exclaimed.

"Yeah," Steneski butted in. "And I been doing some private surveillance on the caper. Others have been away from their desks during the exact moment of the crime, but only one of us is consistently missing at post time. Further, I remember Deeder's artistic talents when he used to doodle composites from a witness's deposition." His gaze trailed to Deeder, Horton's following, and Del's shifting last.

Deeder remained cool, never acknowledging being the focal point of three pairs of accusing eyes. "You'd best keep your suspicions to yourself, Ski. Never know when your old lady might get an anonymous tip and find out where your car's parked on Thursday bowling nights." Ski choked on his beer and nervously wiped the foam from his chin.

"Well, I'll be damned!" Horton's eyebrows shot up at Deeder's innuendo, and all eyes turned on the crimson-faced Steneski. "And all this time I thought bowling was a family sport." Horton chuckled, swiveling on his stool to stare in disbelief at his squirming partner.

The revelation didn't surprise Del much. It was a prime example of why cops ran one of the highest divorce rates of any profession. The temptations were great, and the opportunities ever present. She returned her attention to Deeder. Their eyes met, and she read the confirmation within his—Deeder was the phantom they all longed to be. "Better be careful, Deed," she warned lowly.

"Always am!" He winked, his mug hitting the bar with a slam. "Two more, Mickey." Del knew she'd probably hate herself in the morning, but tonight she'd keep up with Deeder if it killed her!

"Hey, Mick, turn on that thirty-minute magazine show on Channel Six." Horton nodded toward the television mounted up in a corner of the wall. "It's about time for that local gossip columnist. You know, the one with the face like a *Playboy* centerfold and the sexy voice to match. I never miss her."

The bartender set Del's and Deeder's drinks in front of them before pressing the remote control and turning on the television. A few grumbles went up from the jukebox crowd but soon died down. Two minutes' worth of commercials flicked across the screen before the gorgeous gossip columnist Horton liked so much appeared.

"Turn it up a little, Mick. Let's see what Miss March '79 has to say." The volume increased, a mellow but phony voice drifting down to where they sat. Del didn't pay much attention, concentrating instead on lowering the level of her glass in the exact same increments as Deeder.

"And last, but certainly not least, guess what old flame has rekindled?" The lulling voice continued from the box up on the wall. "Who was on whose arm at the fund-raising dinner held tonight for the new music hall? None other than the famed opera celebrity Miss Ramona Valez and our very own debonair legal star, Mr. Mitchell Parrish."

Suddenly Del sat straighter on the stool, her eyes riveted on the screen. There before her was Mitch, poised and smiling, and next to him a beautiful brunette whose striking features could be described only as classic.

"Aren't they a lovely couple?" The sugar comments virtually drooled from the commentator. "It's only this reporter's opinion, but I think reconciliation is in the wind for this attractive pair."

"Well, can you believe that!" Horton gave a low whistle. "Imagine a creep like him with a good-looking gal like that. Man! I'd give my eyeteeth to change places with him. She's a knockout!"

Once the initial shock of seeing Mitch and his attractive date on the barroom set began to wear off, a combination of longing and jealousy started to coil in the pit of Del's stomach. Her hands clenched her mug tighter as the reporter's silly narration droned on.

"If I'm wrong, it would be a sad day for romance and lovers everywhere. The Valez-Parrish love match is dynamite. So here's hoping that the striking couple mend the breach and that my prediction comes true very soon."

Just as the columnist finished up, the camera zoomed in for a close-up. Ramona Valez's hand rested on Mitch's shoulder as she flashed a practiced smile for the audience. And there, on her pinkie finger, was an exact replica of the ring Del had noticed on Mitch's hand the night of their fireside chat. *A gift given to me a long time ago . . . Yes, once she was very special, but only to me. Now . . . she's adored by millions.* Mitch's words on that long-ago night leaped into Del's brain, a chill running the length of her spine. Obviously their past involvement was well known. It seemed clear that everyone in the world knew it except her. What had she been—some convenient in-betweener to fill the gap during a lovers' spat? The accusation was unfair, and she knew it; but at this humiliating moment she didn't feel like being fair. She felt like a damned fool!

"You look like you've seen a ghost." Deeder's perceptive eyes were upon her.

"I need another drink." She didn't even try to hide her agitation as she swallowed the last of her drink and shoved the glass toward the bartender in a silent gesture.

Deeder glanced from her to the television and then wisely fell silent. Horton, oblivious to all else but the luscious dark beauty on the TV, kept up his ranting gibberish.

"It makes you sick when some fancy-breeches uptown mouthpiece gets his pretty kisser plastered all over the set with a gorgeous dame like that. Bet he don't even know how to handle her. She looks like a hot little number. Did you catch those pouty lips? Love 'em when they got that kind of naughty but nice smile." He went on and on, while Steneski, who couldn't get a word in edgewise, merely nodded his head in silent agreement.

"How about those high cheekbones? She's got Indian in her. You can tell. I've heard those squaws are wild, wild! I'd love to find out for sure."

Deeder's mug banged to the bar, but Horton paid no heed. Del noticed but was too busy dying a little inside to react.

"I betcha I could warm her tepee better than Parrish any old day!" Horton bragged.

That tore it! Del couldn't stand to hear another word. "Why don't you shut up, Horton? If I wanted a rundown on your bedroom credentials, I'd ask!" Her fiery glare burned holes clear through him.

"Well, pardon the hell out of me!" He returned her angry look with one of his own.

"It's hard sometimes, Horton . . . real hard." Deeder put his two cents' worth in.

"Well, ain't you two a dandy pair tonight—one with a kink in her pantyhose and the other in his Fruit of the Looms."

Noting the squaring of Deeder's shoulders, Steneski, the peacemaker, jumped in. "Boy! I think this overtime's got us all a little edgy. It's just a goofy show. Hardly important at all." His nervous eyes shifted from one to the other, watching as some of the previous tension began to ease.

"You about ready to shove off, Del?" Deeder motioned to the bartender without awaiting her reply. "Catch you guys tomorrow." He slapped a ten-spot on the bar as Del climbed down from the stool.

"Hey, Del." Horton's voice stopped her in her tracks, her body tensing in preparation for what was to follow.

"You forgot your purse." Horton held out her shoulder bag with an apologetic smile.

With a composing breath she faced him. Though she wanted to be a good sport and return his smile, she just couldn't pull off the deception. Merely a soft "thanks" had to suffice as she turned to catch up with Deeder, who had already made it to the door.

Throughout the drive home it seemed all she could do was rattle about cop shop, and none of it made any sense. One moment she talked of the futileness of their jobs; the next, how she was going to beat out any and all competition on the upcoming exam in order to be the first woman lieutenant in the department.

Deeder let her go, knowing the rhetoric was the defense mechanism by which she evaded what was really troubling her. He hadn't worked with her all this time without having learned a little something about her character. She was a tough cookie, but not quite as hard-shelled as she'd like everyone to believe. He'd seen her face when she looked up at the TV screen in the bar, seen the hurt that flickered into her eyes as she gazed at the videotape of Parrish and his latest girl friend. It was him! He'd known there was a man in her life for the past few months; now he knew who. Parrish wasn't someone he would have chosen for her. As a matter of fact, he was a downright illogical choice, but then, when was love ever logical? he reasoned. The ride to Del's house never seemed so long as she continued to rattle on.

Once inside her town house, Del insisted that he stay for a nightcap. It was as if she couldn't stand the thought of being alone. Deeder complied, the bottle of excellent sour mash whiskey dwindling as they continued to hash over the evils of copping and the rewards of promotion. Halfway through the bottle the conversation finally took a turn toward more personal topics, but to Deeder's surprise he found himself the party being third-degreed.

"What got under your skin back there with Horton?" Del asked, a tiny hiccup following the astute deduction.

"Awww, nothin' really. He just gits on my nerves sometimes, is all." He tried to put her off.

"I know better, Deed. Tell me what's eating at you." She wasn't buying it. From past experience he knew it would save a lot of time if he just answered the question.

"I guess I never told you that my wife's an Indian, have I?" He studied her for a quiet moment and, after the negative shake of her head, he continued. "Yeah, well, she is and really somethin', too. Don't nobody understand me the way that woman does. We been married goin' on twenty-three years, got us a fine-lookin' son and a grandbaby on the way."

He took a long draw of the sour mash and then set it aside. "Course, we've seen our share of hard times. My family never could understand my wantin' to marry her, never could accept our half-breed child. And there's a lot of narrow-minded folks like Horton in this old world. It just gits to me sometimes. But after all is said and done, I wouldn't trade a minute of lovin' her. She's what's made my life worthwhile . . . she and the boy."

"I never knew," Del answered softly.

"Most folks don't. My personal life's my own. I like it that way." He smiled that warm, wonderful smile that told a person he was a lucky man who had it all together. "Sometimes I guess ya gotta make up your mind what ya want in this lifetime, go after it, and tell the rest of the world to go to hell." His gaze fell upon her—knowing and compassionate. "I know what's botherin' ya, Del. I been knowin' for a while. I just didn't know who. I don't care for Parrish much, but I do respect him. Do you?" Having said what he wanted to say, Deeder rose to his feet, hiked his pants over his bloated tummy, and strolled toward the door.

Do you? Do you? The unanswered question swirled in her head. Still curled upon the couch, drink in hand, Del downed the last gulp and then impulsively called out to him. "I'm going to pass that promotional exam come spring, Deed! I'm going to be the best damn lieutenant you've ever seen!"

His head poked back around the corner, a tickled expression on his face, yet concern mirrored in his eyes. "Yeah, hot dog, I figure you'll go after it like a hound to a scent. But if you're not real careful, you're gonna wind up a mighty successful but purely miserable woman. Take your time nursin' that hangover you're gonna have in the morning'. I'll cover for ya. Night!"

An hour later, her head swimming with the liquor and the gossip columnist's phony voice, Del reached for the Princess phone and pulled it beside her into the bed. It wouldn't ring, she knew. But just in case it did . . .

CHAPTER TEN

Del drummed her fingers on the linen tablecloth as her eyes swept the large banquet room. It seemed everyone of any prominence was present to honor the Detective of the Year—the honorable mayor and his City Council, the chief of police and his top brass, distinguished members of the Bar Association, and local philanthropists. Del was especially pleased since the nominee this year had truly earned the award. Usually the honor was bestowed upon some twit of a recipient who had no more conception of what made a good cop than the benefactors who controlled the selection. This year, however, it was different. The winner of the engraved plaque and Rolex watch was none other than her deserving partner, Sergeant Deeder Hanes. Her dark eyes lighted upon him as he sat across from her. He looked uncomfortable as he sat rigid upon the velvet-cushioned chair, trying to ignore the stares directed at him and nervously running a finger inside his stiffly starched collar.

"You really don't want to be here, do you?" Her understanding smile reinforced him.

"Not really. It ain't that I'm not grateful. It's just that I don't go in much for these formal affairs. I'd take a reassignment to graveyards better than havin' to make this speech in front of all these highfalutin dignitaries. You know I ain't much of a talker, Del."

"Maybe not in public, Deed, but you're sure no slouch in private!" Her candid statement instantly alleviated some of the strain on his face. "You'll do just fine, Deed. Just relax and be yourself, and I promise you they'll be comparing Deeder Hanes's easy wit to Will Rogers before the night is out."

"You really think so?" Like an insecure child, he searched her face for reassurance.

"Trust me!" she said affirmatively.

"Yeah, I've heard that one before." He scrutinized her coy expression over the candlelit centerpiece before adding, "Listen, Del, I never did thank you for fillin' in on such short notice for Nemeha. She hated missing this shindig, but the flu's got her down."

"I'm honored that you asked me to come with you, Deed. I know how disappointed your wife must feel, but I brought along my trusty Kodak so she can see how well her husband was received tonight."

"Don't be takin' no pictures, Del. I got enough to be worryin' about without havin' to smile for family snapshots. Besides, I never did take a good picture anyhow."

"Why, Deed, I think you're actually blushing." She laughed softly as the waiter began to place the entrée before them, and the mayor climbed the podium to begin his welcome introduction on behalf of the LEAL (Law Enforcement Appreciation League). His boring speech would allow for at least twenty minutes of respite in which to eat their meal.

The black-jacketed waiter methodically covered his station, serving Deeder's front and center table of honor and then working his way back along his assigned six tables.

"Excuse me, please," he apologized as his elbow accidentally hit the shoulder of one of the guests. The attractive brunette glanced up at him briefly, gave a curt nod, and then returned to addressing the group at the table.

"As I was telling Michel, I plan to make a European tour within a few months. Venice is *absolutamente bello* in the spring," she cooed, leaning closer and linking her arm through her escort's as she talked. The waiter scowled when having to serve from the right because of the intimate barricade in his path.

"I enjoyed your last concert tour very much, Miss Valez," another guest was saying as the harried waiter made the full circle of placements and turned to depart. Mitch's bored gaze followed his weave through the crowded tables as he returned to check on his most important assignment—the guest of honor.

The waiter stopped first at the heavyset gentlemen who, though dressed like all the other affluent and influential guests, looked totally out of place and quite aware of it. Almost trancelike, Mitch's gaze continued to wander along with the conscientious waiter, but suddenly his blue-gray eyes grew alert and electric as he spied the woman the waiter paused beside. He should have expected it but was completely unprepared for it—the sight of Del! He had to fight back an irrational urge to rise from his seat and go to her, had to make himself recall the time, place, and circumstances they were in, had to force himself to remember that, here and now, they were practically strangers with no past and certainly no future. God! The time between had made her even more beautiful!

"There is something that distracts you, Michel?" Ramona's voice recalled him. "Or should I say someone?" Her ebony eyes scanned the distance to the front table and lingered. "She is *muy bonita, mi amor.* An acquaintance of yours?" The casual question held definite undertones.

"We've met." He answered the obvious but ignored the implication. "She's a police officer. Probably the honored detective's partner." Evasively he concentrated on the gourmet meal that was cooling before him.

"Interesting," Ramona replied, then quickly added, "I mean, a woman in law enforcement. It could hardly be considered a very typical or feminine profession. Makes one wonder what sort she is. I always think of a lady officer as rather, how you say, crass and tomboyish." Her unrelenting gaze analyzed his reaction.

"That's a bigoted statement if I've ever heard one. Is there any special reason you're being so nasty, Ramona? Or is it becoming your general nature lately?" His steely gray stare grew accusatory; his tone, censorious.

"Neither, *mi amor.* I withdraw the assumption and apologize if I have offended." She smiled sweetly, sipped her water, and returned to her meal as if the conversation had never taken place. She knew better than to pursue the discussion in his present mood. Once Mitch's attention became drawn back into the dinner chat, she chanced another glance over at the honey-haired blonde who had been the object of his mesmerized focus. *Ahhh,* she mused, *but I suspect that the lady is extremely* importante *to you,* mi amor. *I know. For I've seen that look in your eyes before, but then, it was for me that they shone so!*

The LEAL president's keynote address began above the hum of after-dinner talk and the clatter of dishes being cleared. The normal amount of backslapping took place. The president first commended the department on its excellent record of dedicated service, and then the chief of police reciprocated by thanking the civic organization, and all present in the room, for their unwavering support. It went according to protocol and was predictably boring. Del noticed Deeder's uneasy shift in his chair as he ran a handkerchief across his brow. The tension of the long wait had to be excruciating. It was only when the chief finally announced that he felt especially privileged to be presenting the LEAL award to this year's recipient that Del felt a twinge of excitement. This was the moment, Deeder's finest hour, and her heart fairly burst with pride at the words "And now, without further ado, I present to you our choice for Detective of the Year, Sergeant Deeder Hanes!"

Deeder's and her eyes made contact. He reached across, squeezed her hand, then rose to his feet and climbed the steps to the podium to the applause ringing throughout the room. Once it had died down, the chief gave a brief résumé of Deeder's outstanding contributions to the force. The credits were many and gave great insight into the man being honored this evening. Del considered herself a very fortunate individual to be counted among his friends. A sympathetic smile stole across her sensitive lips as she watched the unaccustomed Deeder withstand the heaps of praise.

During the initial presentation Mitch's attention drifted. Unwillingly his eyes kept resting on Del's lovely profile. He thought about how much he missed her, considered how he could possibly approach her, deliberated on what possible advantage a confrontation between them would gain. When the appropriate time came to applaud, he would snap back to the present and give hand service, but still, his mind kept wandering. Now and then he'd notice a reproachful look from Ramona and would attempt to appease her by returning his regard to the podium and the ceremonies taking place. But then, in a matter of a few seconds, he became lost in thought and the sight of Del once more.

Deeder stepped up to the microphone, gave a nervous clearing of his throat, then looked out at Del and began addressing the distinguished group.

"I was tellin' my partner just before comin' up here that I'm not much of a speech giver." He smiled broadly.

"Well, she reminded me that I ain't never been at a loss for words when it came to voicin' my opinions in private."

The spontaneous laughter that circulated about the room seemed to encourage Deeder. Del could almost see his sigh of relief and the relaxing of his tense shoulders. "I don't mean to insult the LEAL, but I have to be honest when I tell ya that I'm a little uncomfortable acceptin' such an esteemed award for just doin' my job. And that's what it's been for the past twenty-four years—just doin' what I do best and feelin' mighty good about it at the end of the day."

An interested hush settled over the room, as if everyone present realized that this recipient and acceptance speech promised to be out of the ordinary. "But I have to tell ya, it warms my heart to be receivin' this honor at this stage in my life. I'm pretty close to draggin' up. For you civilians out there, that means retirin'. And it's nice to know that over the years a few of the things I've done have been appreciated. I didn't do it for that reason, but it's still kinda nice to be remembered for it. I go back a number of years—to a time when people respected the uniform and the man who wore it. Nowadays it's a little different—it's rare that people acknowledge the job the cop does and even rarer if they thank him for it. That's why this night's so special to me. It brings back fond memories and gives me hope that the rookie that follows in my footsteps will one day know that he, too, was necessary and appreciated."

An instantaneous clapping went up, heads nodding in agreement and low whispers circulating. Deeder's rapport with the audience was almost a magical happening, his honesty and folksy style winning the crowd.

"I'm acceptin' this award"—his hands lovingly gripped the engraved plaque—"on behalf of all my fellow officers. For by honorin' just one, you honor us all. But bein' a little more personal, I'd like to thank y'all for allowin' an old-timer to prove his point—people do still care." Deeder's voice grew sentimentally hoarse as he held up the plaque at arm's length. "This has made it all worthwhile. I thank ya, and God bless!"

As Deeder descended from the speaker's platform, the assembly rose to its feet, applause resounding and a few cheers going up. This truly was Deeder's moment, Del thought, her heart racing with both excitement and pride—at last the well-deserved recognition for his lifetime of dedication. She, too, was on her feet, clapping wildly when Deeder came to the table. Proudly he handed the plaque over for her inspection, but as she took it within her hands, she was totally unprepared for what happened next. His brawny arm slipped about her shoulders, giving her a rough squeeze as he introduced her to the crowd. "My partner!" he exclaimed, a twinkle in his eye and a mischievous grin on his wide lips. And another round of spontaneous applause went up.

"Deeder!" she groaned, desperately trying to retake her seat. The crowd followed suit, the clapping dying down and chairs shuffling as the guests reseated themselves.

"How'd I do?" Deeder asked, pulling his chair closer to hers.

"Great until you pulled that crazy stunt at the end," she whispered, her embarrassed gaze darting about and catching the few dozen pair of eyes upon them. It was then that she locked with the blue-gray eyes that bore down on her. Her skin grew taut, her respiration labored as she looked into the unforgettable eyes that made everything and everyone else vanish from view. Mitch! He was here—in the same room—only three tables and a few feet from her! Quickly she spun about and grabbed for her water glass. She felt the room reel with his presence. Everything became a blur. There was only Mitch, his constancy surrounding her, the sight, smell, and sound of him closing in on her from all sides.

Guests were beginning to bombard the table. Hands being shook, smiles exchanged. Statements were directed toward her—something like "You've got an extraordinary partner, young lady." She could hear herself responding but knew nothing of what she was saying. Her mind could assimilate only one thing—the nearness of Mitch!

She tried to fight the panic that gripped her. *Surely he won't come over,* her mind reasoned as another hand reached out for hers and another nonsensical comment was leveled at her. If only she could get away . . . excuse herself . . . hide in the women's room. Her mind frantically searched for an escape. But her fate was sealed as yet another hand clasped hers and she found herself looking up into the composed black eyes of Ramona Valez. Almost echolike, Mitch's drawl reverberated in her head. "Miss Valez insisted on meeting you. Ramona, this is Sergeant Del Harris."

She wanted to recoil—to break and run—but, instead, heard herself reply coolly, "Miss Valez, how nice to meet you." Her chin lifted, and her toffee eyes held their own as their gazes collided.

"The honor is mine, Miss Harris. It is not often I meet a woman who stirs my curiosity." A certain honesty cut through the heavily accented words which did not elude Del.

"How so, Miss Valez?" she coyly prompted.

"I speak of your profession, of course." The stunning brunette cocked her head as if to say, "But I wonder about much more."

Quickly Mitch broke in, extending a hand toward Deeder with a rushed "Congratulations, Sergeant. I thought your speech was most informative."

Deeder, who had been preoccupied with other well-wishers, suddenly found himself thrust in the midst of a very awkward situation. With a hearty shake of Parrish's hand he tried to run interference for Del. "Thank ya, Counselor. Comin' from you, I consider that a mighty big compliment."

Ramona's attention shifted briefly to Deeder. "I, too, offer my congratulations. I find it most regretful that a man of your ability has not been recognized before this."

"I thank ya for the vote of confidence, señorita, but I'd really prefer less recognition and more pay!"

Deeder's customary bluntness didn't deter Ramona a bit. "I find your directness most refreshing, Sergeant. There is too little of it in this world." Her perceptive eyes moved from Deeder to Del to Mitch. The tension escalated—Mitch looking atypically uneasy, Deeder shifting his weight from one foot to the other, and Del's scathing glance in Mitch's direction confirming Ramona's suspicions.

"I have been admiring your gown all evening. It is very chic. May I ask where you purchased it?" Unknowingly Ramona added to the already complex undercurrents by referring to the crocheted evening dress which had so much significance attached to it: Mitch's gown—the farewell gift of New Year's Eve.

"Do you really think so?" Del asked, hedging. "Funny, but I had almost decided against wearing it. At first I loved this gown, but lately it's lost its appeal. I'm sure you, being a woman, know the feeling. Something can strike your fancy on the spur of the moment and later stir nothing within you at all." Del dismissed Ramona's momentarily confused gaze and met Mitch's head-on. The hidden meaning of her remark was not lost on him. It stabbed at his heart and slashed at his pride.

Deeder virtually cringed. He wished he were anywhere but where he was at the moment. Ramona mentally noted the flicker of anger that flitted over Mitch's face a moment before a mask of indifference froze into place, but then she pretended not to have noticed. The incited reaction only served to reaffirm her earlier deduction: The lady was extremely *importante* to Michel.

"Ahhh, but I understand most perfectly," she replied smoothly. "We women are most fickle. I have a closetful of discarded garments which attests to this. It has been most interesting meeting you both." Ramona's parting smile was perfectly executed; her words were delivered with practiced eloquence. "*¡Buenas noches!*" Her arm linked through Mitch's possessively, and with a curt nod from him they departed.

Deeder noticed the defeated slack in Mitch's shoulders as they walked toward the door. He couldn't help feeling sympathy for him. Del had been harder than usual. In fact, her snippy attitude was a side of her he'd seldom seen.

"A little rough on him, weren't ya?" Somehow he felt compelled to speak up in Mitch's behalf.

"I don't play the game well, Deed. That's all." The note of defeat in her voice and the vanquished look in her eyes as she gazed after Mitch told Deeder all he needed to know—the lady still deeply cared!

"Come on," he said soothingly, wrapping a burly arm around her shoulders and leading her through the crowd. "Let's git the heck out of here and find us a place where we can unwind. How about the Waterin' Hole? It's easy on the mind and the pocketbook. Since the Detective of the Year is doin' the buyin', I figure it's my choice. What d'ya say?" He patted her shoulder encouragingly.

"I say it's your night, and whatever you want goes." She tried to give him a smile, but her breaking heart would allow only a poor imitation. She bit her bottom lip to keep it from trembling, snuggled closer to Deeder's secure bulk, and let him lead her away—away from the disastrous encounter and the unbearable memories it had conjured.

Ramona's hotel room had the usual view of Ocean Drive and the yacht basin, the usual king-size bed with usual laundry-marked linens. The only unusual thing was the foreign feel of her dusky rose skin against Mitch's. It had been a very long time since he'd experienced the sensation, but tonight, no matter how hard he tried, he just couldn't reclaim that old chemistry. Again he attempted to capture what once had been, his hands roaming the Latin lady's nude perfection as his mouth claimed hers forcefully but insensitively. He tried, tried his damnedest, to forget that the mouth he kissed was not naturally responsive like Del's, but rather experienced and demanding as only Ramona's could be. Ramona's stimulating tongue didn't explore with sweet anticipation. No, it was more like rehearsed greed.

Why was he making these comparisons? His mind whirled as his body went through the motions of making love. It wasn't working! It just wasn't the same. God! Why couldn't he replace one gorgeous body with another? Weren't men supposed to be able to do that without the slightest emotional regard? Damn Del for hexing him with feelings he couldn't escape—thoughts he couldn't ignore! Regretfully Mitch released Ramona's eager lips, sighed, then fell back on the pillow, to reach for a glass and the bottle of Chivas once more.

"I'm sorry," he murmured after taking a stiff shot. "I guess I've had too much of this!" He swirled the amber liquid within the glass mockingly.

Ramona cuddled up beside him. The silver moonlight flooding through the opened drapes on the terrace doors highlighted his distressed features. Gently her fingertip traced the deep furrow on his forehead, but still, she did not speak.

"Say something! Anything! I feel like an absolute ass!" He begged to be reproached. After all, this one-night stand had been his idea—a way to salvage his wounded pride. The very least Ramona deserved was to have her needs satisfied, and he hadn't even been able to accomplish that.

"*Desear es fácil; estar enamorado, difícil,*" she murmured affectionately.

"If you've just called me a fool, you're right." He laughed, the sound of his voice as hollow as the faraway look in his eyes.

"No, *mi amor.* What I said was: 'To desire is easy; to be in love, difficult.' " He turned his head from the beautiful face which spoke the truths that at this moment he wished he could deny. Her fingers ran within the thick folds of his hair, soothing as she softly spoke. "We have been acquainted a long time, Michel. Do you believe I know you so little as not to realize when you are trying to forget another woman in my arms? As much as I would treasure taking you into my bed, consoling you for one night, it would serve no purpose. It is not possible to erase current memories by conjuring old ones, *mi amor.*"

Mitch's troubled eyes returned to her serene face. Her raven hair shone like lustrous mahogany in the moonlight, tumbling provocatively over one side of her enchanting face and cascading to her breast. Unconsciously his fingers toyed with the luxurious strands while he silently contemplated her truths. It seemed aeons passed before he, at last, found the appropriate words to say.

"I've been unfair, Ramona. I don't normally manipulate a woman in bed—merely enjoy her." He paused, meeting her gaze with a half smile. "We always had a wonderful time together. It would be a shame to ruin that track record now. Maybe another time, when my head is clear of Scotch and memories?" His palm slid along her neck, then caressed her cheek endearingly.

"*¡Qué lástima!*" She sighed, then pressed her lips to his palm. "Some advice, *mi amigo.* You will find clearing your head of the liquor easier than extricating yourself from the woman who haunts you. Go to her, Michel. If you love her, you must! Pride often comes between men and what they desire most. So few of them learn that it takes *un poquito* to win a woman's devotion forever. It is so simple it often eludes them. Let her know you love her above all else—reassure her of this."

"I only wish it were as uncomplicated as that, Ramona. I find that history repeats itself. Again I'm between a woman and her career, and I can tell you from past experience, it's a loser's position." He propped himself up on an elbow, finished off the last of the Scotch, then swiftly sat up and jerked on his pants.

"Such little resistance, *mi amor.* It is not like you to give up so easily. Try once more. Then, if fate is unkind, return to me, and we will substitute passion for love." Her promising lips brushed the back of his neck lightly before she fell back upon the pillows, pulling the sheet with her. "In some ways our reunion has been *muy bueno,* eh, Michel?" She gave a sleepy yawn, stretching sexily beneath the thin percale covering.

Tucking in his shirt, then grabbing his jacket, he smiled down at her before leaning and placing a farewell kiss upon her sultry lips. "You're not only beautiful but wise. *Adios,* pretty lady."

Their parting had been unbelievably easy. The Latin lady had meant it to be so!

CHAPTER ELEVEN

Del sat at her vanity, aimlessly running the hard-bristled brush through her hair. It wasn't until her scalp began to tingle rebelliously that she realized she'd been repeating the thoughtless procedure for almost an hour—sixty monotonous minutes of just staring into space and mechanically brushing her hair like a wind-up doll. She glanced at her reflection in the mirror. The dark, blank eyes set within the expressionless face really did resemble a lifeless replica of herself. There wasn't the slightest hint of animation—only a porcelain exterior, cold and brittle, which she felt certain would crack into a thousand indistinguishable pieces if she were to touch it. *All the king's horses and all the king's men couldn't put Del back together again.* Her version of the childhood nursery rhyme floated in and out of her head as she sat, as if in a trance, before the mirror. Then, as if afraid to test the analogy, she set aside the brush and turned away from the disturbing reflection.

Mama Cat lay curled upon her bed, contentedly snoozing. Del lay down beside her, idly stroking her fluffy fur and thinking aloud. "No worries, Mama Cat? It must be nice. In my next life I'm coming back as a lonely woman's pampered pet." Her pathetic description of herself brought a sad smile to her lips. *Lonely!* The disparaging word echoed in her head. Before Mitch, the loner aspect of her life had only mildly bothered her. Now it tormented her. God! How she missed him! Seeing him tonight had only reemphasized that fact all the more.

I'm sure he isn't lonely or missing me tonight. The rash conclusion added to her misery. *No, I'm certain Miss Valez will see to it that he doesn't lack for companionship!* Because she was so miserable herself, the very thought of the two of them together made her heartache even more unbearable. Her arm covered her eyes, as if to block out the hurtful pictures her jealousy conjured: Mitch and Ramona . . . laughing . . . teasing . . . kissing . . . making love. She hated them! But no more than she hated herself for the wild imaginings she envisioned. Damn Mitch for ever coming into her life, turning it upside down and inside out and then deserting her to the pain of his withdrawal.

Del moaned, turned onto her side, and fought back the stinging tears that burned her eyes. *Miss Valez can have him back! I don't need him! Don't want him!* The lies spun in her head, their bitterness mingling with the tears that spilled down her cheeks. *But if you're not real careful, you're gonna wind up a mighty successful but purely miserable woman.* Deeder's words taunted her. "I don't think I have a choice, Deeder." She groaned before burying her head in the pillow to muffle the wretched sounds of her crying.

Finally becoming aware that he'd been driving around in circles for the past hour, Mitch pulled off onto the shoulder of the road, turned off the engine, and leaned his arms upon the steering wheel defeatedly. Where was it he wanted to go? He pressed his forehead to the padded rim of the wheel. To Del's—where else? his rational self answered. It would be a futile gesture, he knew—painfully, embarrassingly futile. The wiser Mitch told him to ignore the strong inclination, to do the safe thing and go home and forget the impulse. But some inner voice kept badgering him, telling him to try—try once more. It was Ramona's advice that rang in his head, but there was something more; there was that reasonable doubt to cling to—that all was not lost when two people cared. And Mitch couldn't resist trusting in the miracle of love.

Decidedly the key turned over the engine, and all eight horsepower laid rubber as Mitch made a U-turn and headed for Del's. It was one o'clock in the morning, and his mission, total insanity; nevertheless, he was determined to tempt fate. If he ever needed to be persuasive, the time was now. He'd never been the kind of man who believed in Lady Luck, but if she existed, he prayed she'd smile on him this one time. This was one closing argument he couldn't afford to lose. So much was at stake; two futures hung in the delicate balance, and the unpredictable scales of love could tip either way.

The road became only blurred white-marked lanes that led to Del; stop signs and red lights, obstacles in his path. Speed limits weren't relevant; there was only fast and faster, propelling him toward final verdict that he, the defendant, had to hear. The asphalt miles between him and Del dwindled, and in record time Mitch pulled to a stop in front of her town house. The walk to her front door seemed endless. For the first time Mitch could relate to the true meaning of the prison phrase "the death walk." He hesitated for a dreading second and then pressed his finger to her doorbell again and again.

Del awakened to an incessant chiming. Groggy and stiff, she hauled herself up from the bed and stumbled to the front door. Though too drowsy to care about the late-hour summons, she was alert enough to realize that the repetitious chiming sounded urgent. After she had cracked the door, it took an incoherent second before the shock of Mitch's presence on her doorstep set in. It was an agonizing eternity for him while he awaited the slam of the door in his face or the invitation inside. As she stood immobile and staring at him, he began to wonder if she was going to react at all. Then, suddenly, the singular sound of his name upon her lips beckoned him within. The door closed behind him, and in the dark her silence intensified.

He listened as her footsteps crossed the room, and then he blinked as the den lamp snapped on. Against the brassy light her shapely figure was silhouetted through the gauzy material of her nightgown, and unwillingly Mitch's body reacted. She'd always had that strange sort of power over him, arousing his passion with a look, or a word, and never intentionally. That sensual chemistry between them was inexplainable—instantaneous and irresistible; mysterious and exciting.

"Why are you here, Mitch?" Her voice drifted the distance to where he stood—five softly spoken words that demanded so much!

Because I love and miss you, he wanted to shout. But instead, he held his emotions in check, calmly replying, "Because I think we should talk."

"About what?" That defiant tilt of her chin told him his plea bargaining would not be easy. To his further dismay, she strolled away from the lamplight, shadowing her face and figure once more.

"Us," was all he answered while silently pondering what next to say. There had to be an alternative to begging for clemency. Surely his courtroom strategy wouldn't fail him now! Not at this, the most important moment of his life!

"Us," she repeated lowly. "Correct me if I'm wrong,

Counselor, but I've been proceeding on the assumption that when you last walked out my door, the term 'us' ended." Her voice grew hard and cutting.

Without even being aware, he stepped nearer to her. It was as if he couldn't keep his distance any longer. "Del," he beseeched, "be patient and hear me out."

Her smoldering dark eyes held him at bay. "I'm listening, Counselor. I'm sure whatever you've come to say must be important. I mean, why else would drag yourself away from"—her gaze traveled over him demeaningly—"from your busy social schedule to come here?"

He ignored the suggestiveness of her tone but felt a twinge of hope at her jealousy. "It is important, Del. I want to mend the breach between us. Surely there must be a way to work out our differences if we care for each other." His inquisitive blue-gray eyes searched hers.

"And what makes you think I still care?" Her arms folded over her chest obstinately, but the tremble in her voice betrayed her.

"Because you need me as much as I do you," he answered firmly.

"Not as much as I once thought, Counselor." She flung his words back in his face. Some demon inside her wouldn't allow her to confess what she knew to be true.

"I haven't the inclination or the stamina to play word games with you, Del. But if need is an inaccurate conjecture on my part, try care. We do still harbor feelings for one another, don't we?" He stepped closer to her, so close the scent of his familiar cologne filled her senses.

"At the moment mine are very mixed up. The last time you were here, we both cared, and it made no difference. Why do you think anything has changed? You couldn't live with our relationship then. What makes you think you can now?" Del didn't know what was making her say these things, except that a part of her wanted to hurt him as much as he had her.

"You're not going to give it a chance, are you?" His voice rose with his frustrated anger. "The hardhearted sergeant's going to have her revenge, regardless of what it costs us. Be reasonable, Del. At least meet me halfway."

This was his last plea, and she knew it. She ached to burst free of the trap her flippant words had pinned her in, longed to reach out and caress away his anguish. But what of her? If she took him back without a resolution of their problem, what had she gained? A few more hours in his arms, in his life, and then the pain of separation again? If, at this moment, he reached out and embraced her, she would crumble; if then he kissed her, she would melt. As much as she longed for that, this time their beginning had to be different. Yes, this time there must be concessions on his part. Her surrender couldn't be unconditional.

"When I asked the same of you, to be reasonable and meet me halfway, you refused. Now you expect it from me. Let me tell you what I expect, Counselor. Then, and only then, will we talk!"

"That is?" Mitch's chin squared. There was a limit to his groveling.

"An apology, Mitch. I think I deserve one." She knew she'd asked from him what few had ever gained—a compromising of his pride. Mitchell Parrish *never* admitted he was wrong! But this once he would have to bend or forfeit what future they had. This once she would have it her way or be damned. And damned she would be, to a lifetime of regret, if he refused.

Mitch's hands knotted into fists at his side. She demanded too much. He was sorry for the situation, but not for his stand. "I can't do that, Del, and you know it! We both know that one lousy apology isn't worth the price we're paying, but I'll be damned if I'll say it when I don't fully believe it!" Mitch spun away from her and stormed toward the door.

He couldn't appease her with a lie. He wasn't wrong; she was! His hand gripped the knob, and it turned beneath his fingers with an angry click. The door swung open, the coolness of the predawn air rushing over him. One more step, and it would all be over—one gigantic step, and he'd enter an unfulfilled life that did not include Del.

Helplessly Del watched Mitch's retreat, her heart pounding painfully, the lump in her throat choking off the words she wanted to scream. *No . . . not again . . . Oh, God . . . not again!* If she ran to him . . . stopped him . . . he'd be hers a little longer . . . a day . . . an hour . . . a few precious minutes' more of loving and being loved in return. What was pride compared to this? What was left when he was gone forever? Paralyzed with grief, she turned her head to keep from witnessing his final exit.

The door slammed—an inevitable end to the love affair that should never have been. Like a dramatic rerun of a climactic scene, the nightmare of their first breakup repeated itself. Her heart and will totally broken, Del's shaking limbs crumpled beneath her, and she slumped to the carpet in a miserable sob. The romantic miracle of Camelot had irrevocably ended, and in its place came the maiming ache of heartbreak, the horrible realization that one might have been wrong, and the frightening conclusion that desperate gambles offered no second chances.

"To hell with it!" Mitch's voice reached her as, simultaneously, his gentle hands turned her from the floor into his arms. "It doesn't matter. I'll take you any way I can get you, Del. You may not care for me . . . may not need me . . . but you damn sure want me as much as I want you!"

Dumbfounded, tears staining her cheeks, she looked disbelievingly up into his handsome face. "I . . . I don't . . ." she stammered through quivering lips.

He cut off her words, unaware that she was trying to say that she didn't care who was right or wrong.

"Perjury isn't only criminal," he warned, his persuasive lips brushing hers to silence, "but in this instance inexcusable. You do want me. . . ." His breath came fast with anxiousness. "Tell me that you do, Del." Their misty gazes collided, passion igniting upon contact.

"More than I can tell you," she confessed, her arms slipping about his neck as he lifted her from off the floor and cradled her in his strong embrace. "I want you . . . I want you," she repeated deliriously, her mouth gliding over his neck and cheeks as he walked to the bedroom and laid her upon the satin comforter.

"Show me," he whispered into the moonlit shadows, easing beside her and pulling her against him. Del knew that in their entire lives there would never again be such a moment. Nothing stood between them and all that love encompassed. The mood was as it had never been before, and could never, ever be again.

Her mouth closed over his, at first tenderly, then savoringly, and finally feverishly. In undeniable need, her body pressed closer to him, the sheer material of her gown sliding with each wanton move she made against his muscled length. Alive with loving impulses, each contact between them became sensual—lips, shoulders, thighs, touching and yearning for the pleasurable feel once more. Del's starved lips trailed over Mitch's neck, her slender fingers slowly, methodically undoing the buttons of his shirt, then raking the dark mat on his chest. Her titillating kisses followed. Short, sweet, and stirring, they moved across his throat, over his shoulders, and down his heaving chest, making love to him inch by slow inch.

He groaned aloud when next her tongue began to join the erotic trail, its texture silken as it traveled his flesh and set him on fire. She began to go lower, her cool palms soothing his searing skin. His hands entwined within her hair, stopping the natural course she followed. Gently they led her back to his awaiting lips. Then, teasing her with lingering, promising kisses, he commanded, "Lie back, sweetheart."

She obeyed, settling upon her back and closing her eyes while awaiting his next suggestion. It came swiftly and easily as she felt him slip the gown from her trembling body. His masterful hands felt steady and sure as they began to massage her neck, shoulders, arms, experienced as they kneaded her sides, tummy, and hips, absolutely fantastic as they stimulated her back, buttocks, and thighs. Anywhere and everywhere that he touched, Del responded, her attuned body becoming the instrument that he played. Until Mitch she had never thought herself capable of such responsiveness, but she was learning that there were no barriers, no limits when two people shared mutual feeling and respect.

"You're so beautiful, Del," she heard him whisper. She opened her eyes to the love that shone from within his, and the depth of his sincerity reinforced her. "I've loved you from the start, and I'll love you to the end," he promised in a husky voice, his hand caressing her cheek as his words embraced her heart.

"Show me." She repeated his challenge, pulling him to her as if the gesture would bind him forever. His lips claimed hers in a kiss that spoke of united lifetimes and infinite love. Her body molded to his, silently sheltering his commitment.

"Don't give up on me, Mitch," she begged, clinging to him as tightly as a frightened child. "I'm only just learning to trust." The dormant gypsy he had hinted of long ago emerged. And as he had predicted, it had taken only the the right moment and an understanding man to bring her forth.

"I couldn't if I wanted to. You're a part of me, gypsy." He hugged her close, his strong heartbeat thudding in unison with hers.

"Love me, Mitch," she murmured against his ear. "Love me until nothing else matters anymore."

"I intend to, Del," he pledged. And with those words, Mitch set free that smoldering gypsy soul that he alone had recognized from the start. After rising and removing his clothes, he lay down beside her and began to fulfill his promise. Patiently he coaxed with a velvet touch, soothed with adoring kisses, reassured her with an intimate lullaby until he banished all mistrust and completely won the timid gypsy's heart.

Beneath his body, so warm, so sure, Del's shuddered in total surrender as, at the ultimate moment, he entered her. In the predawn light she could see the euphoric tenseness of his features, feel the tremble that ran the entire length of his body as he experienced the transcending sensation of being sheltered and nourished in her love. With each rhythmic thrust he cleaved to her. The gypsy's passion belonged wholly to him. For it had been he, only he, who had discovered her, tamed her, prophesied her needs, and it would be he, only he, who'd now completely fulfill them.

The desire in Del's eyes became luminous, their fiery glow torching Mitch's sensual moves. Possessively her arm encircled his neck, her sweet, short breaths mingling with his moans. Easing his fevered lips to hers, she stilled his delirium with her alive mouth and drained away his last ounce of self-control. The final moment came swiftly, but mutually, ending with synchronic sigh, a fast embrace, and then the hushed serenity that comes when two people are, at last, at peace with each other.

In the weeks that followed, Mitch and Del were privately inseperable. It was as if the trauma of their past separation had served as a catalyst to bring them even closer together. No matter what time Del's shift ended, she could count on Mitch to be at home and waiting for her. Depending on the hour, she'd *either* find a late supper, a reviving nightcap, or a sleepy kiss and a warm cuddle when she joined him in the bed, and without fail, all were given with a fortifying smile. He was her lifeline, a protected cove which offered shelter from a sea of unrest, a sanctuary where she could safely anchor to make reparations for the discontentment she'd endured. But beyond restoring her, he fulfilled her, in every conceivable way.

Their contentment was almost complete—almost, but not quite. There still remained an unspoken barrier between them—a no-man's-land where one existed from moment to moment and futures hung in limbo. Both Mitch and Del realized the extent of the other's deep feelings, yet each was the product of an era which had indoctrinated them to believe that such feelings should be expressed through sanctioned vows and obligated commitment. Had they been born ten years later, the term "living together" would not be a moral hang-up; but they hadn't been, and it was. Yet, because they each carried the scars of their first philosophical split, both were afraid to approach the subject again. Instead, they pretended to themselves, and to each other, that their moral compromise would mellow and resolve itself with time. In a secret, practical corner of their hearts they both knew better but hoped that time would be kind and fate intervene on their behalf. It was a fool's wish, but then, they lived in a fool's paradise.

After finishing up her last night shift and beginning the drive home, Del found herself pondering the never discussed dilemma while breezing down the freeway. She longed to tell Mitch that her stubborn stand against exposing their relationship had been unreasonably harsh. For over the past few weeks he'd taught her by his unselfish example that personal devotion reaped a happiness that professional dedication could never bring. No more did it concern her what her peers or, for that matter, the rest of the world thought. She loved the enigmatic Mitchell Parrish more than anything else on this earth, and she'd proclaim it to the heavens if it meant keeping him. Let the cynics scoff, the bigots mock them! There was only one person's opinion that concerned her—the man she loved. From him came her strength, and in his eyes lay the only esteem of any worth.

The front porch light shone in welcome as she rolled up into the driveway—another thoughtful consideration on Mitch's part. Del eased from behind the wheel, slammed the door, and quietly entered the still house through the side door. A note rested on the kitchen table. Wearily slinging her purse into a chair, she smiled to herself upon reading his distinctive scrawl: "Leftover Chinese in the oven. If you're in the mood for dessert, wake me up!" Lovingly she set the note aside and then strolled to the oven to turn it off. In her present mood she was inclined to pass over the main course in preference of his latter suggestion. Expectantly she made her way to the bedroom, the deep breaths of Mitch's tranquil slumber greeting her. In the dim light that filtered in from the bathroom, she observed his peaceful repose. Bared to the waist, his chest rose and fell in an easy, rhythmic pattern, yet beneath the smooth symmetry of his physique lurked a latent prowess. Similarly, his tousled hair fell lazily across a tapered brow, its rascality contradicting the choirboy serenity of his somnolent features.

Not having the heart to awaken him, Del tiptoed to the bathroom and stripped to take a shower. Somehow a steaming shower at the end of her day had become a ritual. She loved her job, but there were times she felt the need to cleanse herself of the murk she encountered daily.

Turning on the pelting spray, she stepped beneath it, dousing her curls and letting the invigorating warmth rush over her body. Then, leaning forward, her palms on the wet tile, she let the force of the water hit the small of her back in order to relieve its ache. With a deep sigh she closed her eyes and savored it. The minutes flew by as she unwound beneath the pulsating spray.

With a sharp crack the glass door of the shower flew open, Del's startled eyes jerking up to clash with Mitch's amused ones. "You scared me," she managed between excited breaths.

"And you aroused me, in more ways than one." He grinned, stepping inside the small cubicle. Instantly the steamy enclosure became energized with his naked presence.

"Since you're here . . ." An enticing smile skittered across Del's moist lips as she held out the fragrant bar of soap to him.

Slowly the soap turned within his hands, a creamy lather billowing as his enthralled eyes ran the length of her curved wet torso. Deliberately he psyched her for what was to follow while tracing the meandering drops as they twined seductively down her sleek perfection and spilled at her feet. The creamy contact of his hands upon her skin sent a thrill along the back of Del's neck. Every sensitive nerve beneath her primed flesh tingled at his gentle stroking, and as his lips sought hers, his rock-hard body pressing her back against the moist tiles, their world became a mélange of sensuousness—pulsing water and throbbing hearts; the scents of lavender soap and musky passion; the liquid friction of wet skin against skin, smooth and salacious; and the stimulation of probing, misty kisses which mingled with the vaporous atmosphere until creating a torrid climate. It was the longest, most fascinating shower of her life—one of those crazy spur-of-the-moment happenings which cannot be recaptured but is never forgotten.

Many pleasurable minutes later Mitch guided her spent form from the shower stall. His hands worked magic as they patted her dry and snugly cocooned her in the fluffy towel's warmth. Then, drawing her turned back intimately against him, he enfolded her tightly within his strong arms. Adoringly his cheek nestled against her damp hair. They stood for a long moment, merely enjoying the afterglow of love and the secure feel of each other. At last, with a regretful sigh, he spoke.

"I guess now's as good a time as any to tell you that I won't be here when you get home tomorrow." His casual statement shook Del to the core. Her body went rigid beneath his touch, her head shooting up and her bewildered eyes engaging his steady ones in the mirror.

"Why? What's the matter?" The dejected tone of her voice practically lurched his heart from his chest. Swiftly he turned her within her arms, clutching her close.

"Nothing, sweetheart." He hurried to assure her. "It's business, is all. I'm needed in Dallas for a week or so."

He felt the relieved shudder that passed through her slim body and steadied her by running his hand into her hair and cradling her head against his shoulder. Her vulnerability stabbed at his conscience. Had he done this to her? Reduced her to the uncertainty of a backstairs mistress? It had never been his intention; in fact, quite the opposite was true. He loved Del, needed her, not waiting in the shadows, but by his side, every hour of every day. A wetness trickled onto his chest, her tears scalding his skin and scourging his heart. He didn't dare force her to look up, knowing the extent of her pride and respecting it.

"I'll be on the move a lot, so you'll have to wait for me to get in touch with you." He felt her nod against his shoulder. "And when I come back, we'll talk, Del. I think it's time we reevaluate our future. Maybe then we can eliminate the uncertainty I just witnessed on your face. Have faith in me, Del." His own voice tremored with emotion as his fingers tightened anxiously within her hair.

Through a blur of tears she noted deep grooves of strain that marked his taut features. Reflexively her arms locked about his neck and drew his lips to hers. Though an immediate solution remained out of reach, momentarily, his doubts were quelled. Their love was not easy, but then nothing worth having ever was. At least this much he would take with him.

CHAPTER TWELVE

Overtime was becoming a way of life—fourteen-hour stretches of trying to clear practically doubled caseloads. An undeclared street war had erupted, and suddenly Corpus's finest found itself in the middle of a major offensive. Local elections hovered in the winds, and spiraling crime statistics became a front-running issue for every glib-tongued candidate seeking public office. Daily bombardments of political propaganda besieged the department from all sides; verbal assaults of "ineffectiveness on the streets" and "corruption from within" were constantly leveled at the administration. But to Del and Deeder, and the hundred or so other officers who cruised and got bruised on the streets, the guerrilla warfare took on a much more personal note. For it was only their very thin blue line, weary and handicapped, that stood between the uncomprehending citizenry and the criminal elements each hour of every day.

This particular evening, after having put in a solid twelve hours, Deeder and she shortcutted through the barrio sector and headed back in. Bone-weary, Deeder elected to ride shotgun in order to catch a few winks. A light drizzle had begun to fall, and the windshield wipers thumped above the radio traffic droning within the sedan.

Deeder and she weren't communicating much. There just didn't seem a whole lot left to say. It'd been a lousy day, and it was going to be a long report-writing night.

Deeder shifted uncomfortably, rubbed his fatigued eyes, and then glanced out onto the neon-lit streets. "They're up to no good." He gestured with a nod of his head at a gang of youths congregated outside a corner pool hall.

Del decelerated slightly. "Do you want to check them out?"

"Hell, no!" he grumbled, again nodding for her to proceed on by. "Ain't no sense in us lookin' for trouble. It's been findin' us well enough." They sank back into an exhausted silence as exchanges continued between dispatching and the patrol units.

"Ah, one-Baker-six, robbery in progress . . . forty-two hundred block Wittier Drive at the Value Liquor Store."

"Clear . . . about five minutes away . . . will handle." The nonstop calls kept rolling in.

"Sounds like patrol's got a hot 'n' heavy night." Deeder yawned and stretched his arms above his head. "Young fellas' work—quick reflexes 'n' a mite more stamina than I got anymore."

"That's just the tiredness talking, Deed. You can still keep up." Del glanced at his profile. It wasn't like Deeder to be so pessimistic.

"Nope! Can't handle the legwork no more. But I can still give a hot dog a run for his money when it comes to this." His chubby index finger tapped his temple.

Her sincere "I'd put you up against the best of them, Deed," produced a beaming smile on his haggard face, but quickly he shelved the praise.

"Pull over at that drive-in grocery across the street. I'm fresh outta Skoal."

She sighed but refrained from lecturing him on the repulsiveness of dipping. Carefully Del weaved the sedan across the potholed parking lot and rolled to a stop beneath a gaudy sign that blinked "Quik-Stop—Burritos and Cold Beer."

"Won't be a sec," Deeder promised, opening the car door and easing his cramped form upright.

"You know that stuff's hazardous to your health." She couldn't resist a word of disapproval.

"Yeah, but I'm gittin' too old to be sweatin' the small stuff." The door slammed to; his bulky figure swaggered up to the smudged-glass doors of the run-down grocery.

Del turned off the engine and rolled her stiff neck from side to side. Deeder's pit stops always annoyed her. For no matter how pressed they were for time, he'd always find an excuse to squander away some of it.

"Two-Charles-ten . . . domestic disturbance . . . six-one-one-six Polk . . . shots reported fired."

"Ah, two-Charles-ten . . . clear." The night's calls kept her company, her eyes roaming the littered parking lot out of habit as she awaited Deeder's return.

He was taking his sweet time, she thought, leaning over to the rearview mirror and raking her fingers through her hair. Her makeup could use a touch-up, but at this point who cared? She sighed, settled back, and continued to wait. One more time the neon sign flashed, and with it came the sound of a gunshot—as instantaneous as the blinking light, and its identification incontrovertible in Del's mind. Reflexively her hand slid into the opened purse beside her and gripped the Chief's Special firmly. Then, whipping open the car door, she sprang clear in readiness.

The glass doors of the grocery flew open, a male figure backing clear and then turning on his heels to begin flight. Gun raised, Del assumed a firing position, shouting authoritatively, "Halt! Police!"

From under the blinking sign the suspect's motions

appeared disjointed, but clearly Del saw him turn, the gleam off his gun barrel, and a flash of explosive fire. The windshield shattered just as she ducked behind the hood of the car. She could hear fleeing footsteps pounding across the parking lot. Keeping her head down, she ran the length of the sedan. Then, in one smooth, fluid motion, she rose up in a shooting stance, identified herself once more, and fired.

The shadowed figure spun with the impact before hitting the pavement in a flutter of currency that spilled from the paper sack he dropped. Del eased out from behind the car, cautiously sprinted the space between them, and secured the gun which lay beside him.

The past few seconds had been automatic, drummed-in training taking precedence, but now reactionary emotion began to sift into Del's brain. The original shot had been fired from within the store, and Deeder wasn't backing her up! Icy dread began to knot in the pit of her stomach as she turned and broke for the front doors of the grocery.

A couple of terrified onlookers stood dumbfounded in her path. With a solicitous grip on one's jacket, Del breathlessly ordered him to stay with the fallen man on the parking lot. Then, as she burst through the doors, her searching gaze took in the immediate scene in one desperate scan. There, lying on the dirty linoleum, surrounded by shocked patrons, was Deeder—a crimson stain on the front of his white shirt and his face contorted in pain. Del's heart constricted.

"Stand back!" she ordered, pushing through the gawkers and ignoring the onslaught of half English, half Spanish accounts directed at her. In a clean jerk she removed her blazer, rolled it into a pillow as she dropped to her knees, and placed it under his head. Astonished disbelief was mirrored in his eyes as he looked up into her concerned face. He grimaced when she checked his wound.

"Don't worry, Deed," she assured him. "I'm going to get you help!" Not wanting to leave him even long enough to radio for assistance, she combed the sea of faces above her. "Someone call the station and tell them we need ambulances and backup units out here right away."

"*Sí,* señora, I can do this," came the immediate response. Del's eyes were glued on the dark, hazy face above. "Hurry, please!" With an acknowledging nod the Hispanic moved out of sight, and Del's gaze lowered back upon Deeder's pale face once more.

"I should have been with you," she murmured for his ears alone.

"When'd I ever need you to help me buy a can of Skoal?" he whispered hoarsely through a weak smile. A hurtful cough racked his body, dissolving his minimizing pretext. The fingers of his right hand clamped the front of her silk blouse in unspoken agony. Del ached to move him off the grimy floor but knew it was impossible.

"You were right," he confessed in a voice so low she could barely hear him.

"About what?" She leaned closer to catch his shallow words.

"The stuff's plumb hazardous to your health . . ." She wanted to scream at his attempt to satirize the grave situation but instead gave him the smile he was seeking.

His grasp upon the front of her shirt tightened; so did the strings on Del's heart. She knew it was bad, but she had to believe that like so many times in the past, she and Deeder would ride it out. Again she looked into his eyes, but this time she felt like an intruder on a private moment between a man and his maker. Within the glazed pools she saw his frightened reluctance to submit to a hovering limbo.

Every nerve in Del's body froze. In her catatonic state nothing was real—not the sound of excited Spanish and shuffling feet, or the pallet of strewn candy wrappers and cigarette butts, or the faint, spicy smell of warmed-over burritos and the distant wail of sirens. For if she had admitted that these insignificant things existed, she would then have had to acknowledge the reality of the moment and the distinct possibility of losing the man she cradled in her arms, and this she could not do.

Unknowingly her hand enclosed his. The fatalistic cop within her knew that Deeder teetered on the precarious brink of death, but the friend just wouldn't allow herself to believe that the time was at hand for their long-standing partnership to dissolve. She grasped his hand more tightly, as if the insubordinate gesture could countermand an authority much higher than hers, as if her vital force would transfer itself to Deeder and stave off the coldness that was beginning to claim him. Her whisper was both a mandate and a fervent prayer. "Please . . . oh, please, Deeder, don't let go. . . ."

Sirens shrieked to a halt outside. Doors slammed, authoritative shouts went up, and feet scurried across the asphalt parking lot. But these, too, were not real. Nothing was real except the light squeeze of her fingertips by Deeder. He'd responded. . . . Dear God! He'd responded.

Another touch entered her consciousness as a voice that was strangely like Horton's came from out of nowhere.

"Move aside, Del. We gotta roll."

Strong hands clasped her upper arms, raising her to her feet and clearing the way for the paramedics, who worked feverishly over Deeder. She ran a hand through her disarrayed curls in a stunned fashion. Uncomprehendingly her dazed eyes swept the store's interior, taking in the sights, smells, and sounds that she'd earlier denied until clashing with the irrefutable truth in Horton's eyes—this was the united fear they all lived with, the one call none wanted to make.

"Clear this place. I don't want anybody gawking at him!" Her acid tone sounded odd even to herself.

"Sure, Del," preceded Horton's monotoned commands. "Okay, okay, this ain't no sideshow. Move back and make room." In the midst of the commotion and before Del could react, Deeder's limp form was loaded onto a stretcher and whisked out the door.

Horton's arm slipped about her stiff shoulders as he directed her unsteady legs toward the door. With one swing of glass they stepped out into the cool drizzle and the chaotic sounds of a robbery wrap-up—muffled radio garble coming from the units, swirling bubble tops, the hysteria of the curious, and the dispassionate drone of cops trying to unmuddle the mess.

Del's gaze was riveted on the limp suspect also being attended to by medics. "How is he?" A note of regret crept into her voice.

"Just a scratch," Horton reassured her. "You missed the ten ring by a couple of inches."

Del's gaze panned to the ambulance—the bang of the back doors as they were slung open and the clank of the stretcher being loaded. "I'm losing my stomach for this business, you know?"

Horton squeezed her shoulders. "Come on, Del, snap out of it. If ever Deed needed a backup, it's now." His secure grip about her waist hustled her toward the back of the ambulance. "Hold up . . . she goes!" he commanded while boosting her inside. There was only time for a glimpse of Horton's distraught face before the doors slammed shut and the ambulance lurched forward.

"Radio ahead that we've got a gunshot wound—right quadrant of the chest area," the medic ordered the driver. "Tell 'em vital signs poor—blood pressure low and failing, respiration irregular, shock setting in. Recommend a thoracic standby."

Del crouched down beside Deeder, helplessly watching as he labored for breath beneath the oxygen mask. The strangled sob in her throat almost choked her as she brushed his clammy forehead with a trembling hand. *That stuff's plumb hazardous to your health!* Deeder's words echoed in her head. A silent scream tore through her heart. *Live, DEEEDERRR! Live!*

The surgery waiting room was dimly lit and, except for Del, vacant. As she paced the tiled length of the lounge, the lump in her throat kept expanding, much like time since they'd wheeled Deeder through the swinging doors marked "No admittance." Her valiant fight for emotional control kept waning as her tormented mind vacillated between the sweet of the past and the bitter of now. She suffered her own private purgatory, recalling the special moments between her and Deed—moments that only they two had shared and would remember.

Del hugged her midsection to still its cramping. She came to stand before the picture window. A slow patter of rain continued to shroud the streetlamped city, its sound dirgelike when blending with the night shadows. Del's delicate features grew stony, her palms damp. She felt so angry, so empty, so guilty.

Angry because a man doesn't forfeit his life for a lousy can of Skoal! It was ironic, unacceptable, and foul. What possible reason could there be? Mitch . . . if only he could be with her, her grieved mind cried. His words would be wise . . . consoling. He could find some logic in this madness, explain the rhyme and reason so that she could better accept . . . Accept what? That some punk had gunned down Deeder for a stinking $73. *Why, God? Why?*

Empty when flashes of Deeder flicked through her head until even the singular smell of him became pungent in her brain—the odd blend of tobacco and Old Spice. In her mind's eye she saw the rascality of his smile in the health food shop; the phantom's confirmation in his eyes at the Waterin' Hole; an image of the old veteran holding up his cherished plaque and saying, *This has made it all worthwhile. I thank ya, and God bless!* The back of her hand wiped across her eyes, her breath coming labored and painful. What if Deeder didn't pull through? How could she function without him? Why, after this inexcusable waste, would she want to? A spasmodic shudder passed over her. Del shook it off, stiffened, and stared into the night. Mitch . . . how she needed him—his protective arms about her, holding her up, sustaining her through this, the most tragic moment in her life.

Guilty. It was the only word which could describe how Del felt every time she relived the nightmare of her helplessness at that crucial moment when she'd heard the shot. Maybe if she hadn't been so tired, her reflexes would have been quicker. She might have been alert to a potentially dangerous situation when they'd first rolled up. But more than this, it was her irrational reaction to the situation that swathed her in guilt. For some ludicrous reason she partially blamed Deeder. If he hadn't insisted on that stop at the drive-in, none of this insanity would be happening. She resented him for involving her in and making her witness his tragedy. Del cupped her hands to her mouth to smother the grief. God! Was she losing her mind? Deeder was in a surgery room, fighting for his very life, and she was feeling sorry for herself.

The doors to surgery swung open. Del started. Expectantly she looked at the scrub nurse who scurried past. Nothing. No sign. Forlornly she sank onto one of the couches and laid her head back. How long had it been? Thirty minutes? An hour? Her fingers dug into her palms as Deeder's words swam in her head. *It's almost enough to make an agnostic out of a believer.* "Deeder . . ." His name was a imperceptible moan.

Hearing muffled voices in the corridor, she forced her head up and swiped at her blurred eyes. Horton appeared at the doorway, his escorting hand on a petite woman's elbow as he led her to Del. *After all is said and done, I wouldn't trade a minute of lovin' her. She's what's made my life worthwhile. . . .* Deeder's legacy of love swirled in Del's head as she arose and came forward. She clasped the gold-banded hand of Nemeha, her few words giving a quick assessment of the situation. "He's still in surgery. No word yet." There was an understanding nod, at which Del felt totally inadequate. With a squeeze of Nemeha's hand, she looked up at Horton. "We could use some coffee. Would you mind? Without even hearing his reply, she urged Nemeha toward the couch, taking a place beside her and never releasing her hand.

They sat in silent company for a few moments until Nemeha's voice finally intruded. "Did you know that Deed affectionately refers to you as his 'better half'? He's very proud of you, Del."

At her solicitous tone Del turned to face the dark eyes that spoke of fidelity, honor, tribulations, and joy. Her heart thudded in her chest. Instinctively the older woman's arms opened, and for the first time Del released the hold she'd imposed upon herself. Against the fragile shoulder that supported her, the sorrow spilled from Del in uncontrollable waves. "I'm sorry . . . I'm sorry . . ." she murmured incoherently.

"But you have nothing to be sorry for. You did all that can be asked. The rest is in another's hands. It would sadden Deed to see the tears you shed. We must be strong." Nemeha patted Del's shoulder.

With a drained sigh Del straightened and collected herself. "I feel very foolish. I should be comforting you."

"It is unnecessary, Del. Deeder's strength fortifies me. You see, he knows much of simple things, like love and worth. To those he cares for, he gives a code to live by—a kind of love that has no regret. I entrust myself to that love." She actually smiled. "And I have faith in it," she added with serene confidence. "So should you."

Del felt a strange calmness come over her. The peace Nemeha instilled lingered as Horton appeared with the coffee. No sooner had he passed them the cups than the surgery doors swung open and a haggard-looking doctor in faded greens stepped forth. Slowly Nemeha rose as both Del and Horton searched his face in prediction of the next words.

"Mrs. Hanes?" The doctor pulled off his skullcap and wearily rubbed the back of his neck.

"Yes," Nemeha answered, her voice calm, yet her hands clasping the tiny crucifix about her neck for support.

"Your husband's come through the surgery like a trooper. He has a few hurdles ahead and, a long convalescence, but otherwise, the prognosis is good. He's a fortunate man."

Del met Horton's eyes, unaware of the tears of sheer joy which tracked her strained face. He'd made it! Deeder had been spared.

"You can see him, but only for a moment," the doctor was saying. "I'm afraid the other visitors must wait until he's stronger." Nemeha turned, her Indian autumn eyes expressing her gratitude before her small form vanished through the swinging doors. It was over! The nightmare was over! Del never even realized the involuntary collapse of her body against the brace of Horton's arm.

Twice during the drive home Del had to pull off the road to regain her composure. Never in her thirty-five years had she been so completely depleted, yet, crazily, never more aware of the essence of life itself. Deeder's close encounter had vividly emphasized the preciousness of time . . . beautiful, sweet time . . . and, more important, the costly manner in which it was wasted. In the same vein, there was a repetitious thought which kept churning in Del's head—an aching need to be cradled once more within Mitch's steadfast embrace.

It was nearly 4:00 A.M. as she eased onto the deserted side street leading to her town house. Weary of body and spirit, she was as lonely as the hour. She steered in a haze when there, at the end of the road, glowed a beckoning beam of hope—only a tiny porch light in the distance, but a ray of comfort in her heart. Mitch waited for her at home. As if in answer to a prayer, he waited.

Del rolled up into the drive and lurched to a halt. In almost a near panic she sprang from the car and began fumbling in her purse for a key as she all but ran the distance to the porch. She hadn't even cleared the steps when the door swung open and she found herself enfolded within Mitch's sure arms. Wordlessly he pulled her inside and closed the door. She clung to him as he nestled his cheek within her tousled hair, whispering, "I've been so worried, Del. I heard sketchy radio reports on my drive back from the airport. When they finally released Deeder's name, I knew that you had to be the other officer involved." She could feel the tremble in his hands as he clasped the sides of her face and raised her misty eyes to his. "You're all right?" His voice was ladened with concern.

A confirming nod was the best she could manage.

"Deeder?" he asked softly.

"He's going to make it." She sighed. A secure arm encircled her waist, and she found herself looking into blue-gray depths whose calm strength absorbed her despair.

"Oh, Mitch, I needed you so." The words came softly and spontaneously.

"I know, sweetheart. I wanted to be with you, but . . ." She pressed a fingertip to his lips.

"Hold me, Mitch . . . please, just hold me," she begged. As reflexively as her sigh, his strong embrace enfolded her.

"For a lifetime, if you'd let me." Like his comforting caress, his pledge supported her.

"How long is a lifetime, Mitch?" The uncertainty in her voice yearned for reassurances.

"Too short to have wasted any of it, the way we have." He seconded her unspoken thought, hugging her closer until the tremble in her body subsided.

"I'm not certain I believe anymore, Mitch." The resignation in her voice spawned a compassionate ache within him. He embraced her closer still. "After tonight . . . that eternity of holding Deed in my arms . . ." Her voice broke. Consolingly Mitch patted her as he swayed to and fro. He knew that if he didn't allow her to unburden the angry frustration, a portion of Del would become lost in a secret abyss from which he could never again retrieve her.

"We're so alone out there, Mitch," she uttered despondently. "You can pray . . . question . . . damn it all, and none of it makes any difference. To hell with it! Who needs the struggle?" She sobbed against his shoulder.

Mitch gave her a moment to release the hurt, then tipped her chin and kissed away her tears. "You do," he softly admonished. "Granted the injustices are many, and the times you win out, few, but they're significant, Del. Don't ever stop believing in that. It's all right to become disillusioned." Reassuringly he stroked her wet cheek with the back of his hand. "It happens to the strongest of believers at one time or another. But never, ever give up the dream. If you sell yourself short, you'll never know what one lone believer might have accomplished." His eyes locked with hers, their naked sincerity a catalyst of encouragement. "Take the lieutenant's exam . . . add a little clout to the dream and begin the slow work that will eventually turn things around. I'd be disappointed if you did any less." There was an intensity about his smile.

Del clutched him close and buried her face against his neck. "What would I do without my realistic counselor?" She sniffed, her lips snuggling the scented curve of his skin.

"Since I never intend for you to find out, the question's irrelevant, my love." He chided her in words more mellow than the deep sentiment expressed.

During that profound moment all traces of doubt vanished. In its stead sprung a wordless bond that no worldly force could ever dissolve.

At last he released her. Holding her out at arm's length, he studied her, an odd expression on his face. For the first time Del noted the weariness that hollowed his eyes. She ran a fingertip along the dark crescents. "You're worn-out," she murmured.

He pressed her hand to his cheek. "We both are, but we have to talk, Del. Come, let's sit down." His hand locked about hers and led her to the lounger in the den. Sinking to the cushion, he pulled her with him onto his lap. There was a seriousness about him that stirred an unknown apprehension within Del.

Compulsively she cradled her head against his shoulder before asking, "What is it, Mitch?"

She felt the deep breath he took. Her emotions stretched beyond endurance; her apprehension spiraled to panic. She closed her eyes as he began to speak.

"My business in Dallas took a strange twist, Del. I've

been approached about running for the junior seat in the Senate this fall."

The unexpected news startled her upright. "Are you considering it?"

"Yes," he answered firmly.

"You'd seriously contemplate giving up such a successful law practice? But why, Mitch?" Del was truly baffled.

"Instead of challenging the law, I'd like to try my hand at reforming it. I think I have a good chance to win, and at this stage of my life the change appeals to me."

Del's gaze dropped, along with her hopes. The change that appealed to him held no enchantment for her. It would mean extended separations. Though the thought terrified her, she knew, in all fairness, she had no right to stand in the way of something he truly wanted.

"Well, it sounds like too good an opportunity to pass up." She forced a shaky smile while tracing the edge of his opened collar with fingertip. "I think you'll make an outstanding junior senator." She tried to sound convincing.

He caught her nervous fingers, enclosed them tightly within his own, and pensively touched them to his lips. "And what would you say to becoming the senator's wife?"

Del's eyes lifted disbelievingly to his. "I may not have told you or shown you as often as I should have, but I love you, Del . . . more than I ever thought possible. Rebel or conformist, ostracized or eulogized, I need you beside me always." Adoringly his lips brushed hers as he coaxed, "Your verdict, Del. Give me an answer."

Her breathless sigh of "yes" became smothered in the flame of their kiss. Endearing and lingering, the igniting contact of their lips expressed a devotion beyond mere words. Mitch's hands slipped within her honey hair, guiding, drawing, prolonging her kiss. It was the alpha and omega; the beginning of sweet, languid fulfillment; the end of a lonely search.

When, at last, their lips parted, it was Del who managed to speak first. "I'm not altogether sure that I'll make a first-rate wife for an aspiring politician. We both know I'm terribly opinionated and equally as ambitious."

Her candid remark produced a idolizing grin upon his face. "I wouldn't have it any other way. You're such a pessimist. Look on the bright side—conservative or liberal, at least, we're both Republicans."

The coquettish tilt of her head and the mischievous sparkle in her dark eyes warned him. "I should have known." He laughed, pulling her nearer with a playful hug. "Heaven help us! The gypsy's a Democrat!"

[illegible] as the argument [illegible]
[illegible]

[illegible]

[illegible] equally [illegible]

Her candid words prompted a mocking grin upon his face. "I wouldn't have it any other way. [illegible]
[illegible]
[illegible]

[illegible] should have known." [illegible]
[illegible] God help her [illegible]

LOOK FOR NEXT MONTH'S
CANDLELIGHT ECSTASY ROMANCES ®